Ultimate Python Libraries for Data Analysis and Visualization

Leverage Pandas, NumPy, Matplotlib, Seaborn, Julius AI and No-Code Tools for Data Acquisition, Visualization, and Statistical Analysis

Abhinaba Banerjee

www.orangeava.com

First published: April 2024
Published by: Orange Education Pvt Ltd, AVA™
Address: 9, Daryaganj, Delhi, 110002, India

275 New North Road Islington Suite 1314 London,
N1 7AA, United Kingdom

ISBN: 978-81-97081-91-0

www.orangeava.com

Dedicated To

My Beloved Mom and Dad:
Dipti Banerjee and Ajoy Kumar Banerjee
My Strength and Support System

About the Author

Abhinaba Banerjee holds a Master of Science in Big Data Analytics for Business from IESEG School of Management, Lille, France, and a Bachelor of Technology and Master of Technology in Electronics and Communication Engineering from MAKAUT (formerly West Bengal University of Technology), Kolkata, India. He has worked with Fintech and social-media startups in France and is currently involved with the Government of Andhra Pradesh as a Data Analyst. He has also published a few research papers in the field of Communication Engineering and Signal Processing.

He frequently shares blogs on Medium, creates projects, and posts on social media platforms like Twitter. You can find him on Twitter/X at @abhi2652254.

During his free time, he enjoys listening to podcasts on history, technology, and horror.

About the Technical Reviewer

Sarika is a versatile Data Scientist with over 11 years of experience across various domains. With a PG Diploma in Machine Learning and AI from IIIT Bangalore and a Master's in ML and AI from Liverpool University, she has a solid foundation in statistical analysis, machine learning, and data visualization. Currently working with a leading tech company, Sarika swiftly ascended through the ranks due to her exceptional analytical skills and attention to detail. She has dedicated her career to ensuring the accuracy, reliability, and efficiency of data-driven solutions, from developing predictive models to optimizing decision-making processes. In addition to her technical skills, Sarika is an effective communicator and collaborator, bridging the gap between technical and non-technical stakeholders.

Outside of work, Sarika is passionate about staying abreast of the latest developments in data science and technology. She shares her expertise through blogs on a variety of topics, including machine learning algorithms and data visualization. Sarika has participated in several hackathons, using her expertise in data science, machine learning, and artificial intelligence to develop creative solutions and prototypes.

In her free time, Sarika enjoys exploring the outdoors, working out at the gym, and spending quality time with family and friends. Her commitment to a balanced lifestyle reflects her values of discipline, perseverance, and holistic well-being.

LinkedIn Profile: https://www.linkedin.com/in/sarika-srivastava-3553708a

Medium: https://sarika-srivastava.medium.com/

GitHub: https://github.com/sarika1101/

Acknowledgements

Starting the journey of writing *Ultimate Python Libraries for Data Analysis and Visualization* has been the best task of my professional writing career so far, and I must say that I have enjoyed it to the fullest. I am very much thankful to the communities, the tool creators, and other writers without whom I couldn't have completed the book as I wanted it to be.

To begin, many thanks go to the Data community and the wonderful professionals who have significantly contributed to my knowledge and provided the foundation necessary for writing this book. Special thanks to the relevant Data Analysis GitHub repositories, the Python documentation at https://docs.python.org/3.10/library/index.html, and some real-life projects that helped me understand the ins and outs of the contents of the book. Moreover, the technical reviewers' finest attention to technical details and theory-based explanations were invaluable inputs. Their dedication and expertise have been an asset in improving the contents of the chapters and maintaining the quality.

To my family, thank you for your continuing support. Specifically, I want to express deep appreciation to my mother, Dipti Banerjee, whose constant encouragement has been a real saver throughout the writing journey. I would also like to thank my father, Ajoy Kumar Banerjee, for his anchoring support throughout this endeavor.

To everyone at the publication house who has contributed in various capacities, your collective efforts have helped make things perfect day by day. I appreciate the collaborative spirit that has contributed to the creation of *Ultimate Python Libraries for Data Analysis and Visualization*.

Finally, to the readers, thank you for choosing this book as your go-to resource for learning. May it be a valuable companion on your journey to mastering Data Preparation and Analysis using Python.

Preface

In the world of Data Analysis using various coding and no-coding tools, things are evolving faster than ever. Therefore, keeping up with the latest tools, technologies, and tools is imperative for building and contributing to good projects. So, let's embark upon *Ultimate Python Libraries for Data Analysis and Visualization* – where you, the readers, will learn about Data Analysis in depth using various real-life projects and apply them in your workplace, build personal projects, and improve your daily life using various code, low-code, and no-code tools.

This book comprises nine chapters that will help you learn about the nitty-gritty of data preparation, data preprocessing, data analysis, and data visualization comprehensively. It covers a wide range of topics, presenting various topics step by step. Whether you are a professional developer looking to expand your skills by building projects or a fresher willing to learn and apply your knowledge in data analysis, this book has something for everyone.

Chapter 1. Introduction to Data Analysis and Data Visualization Using Python: The chapter starts with an introduction to the topic of data analysis and visualization, the importance of data analysis, and the role of data analysis in decision-making. It covers the main steps of the data analysis process, details on data visualization, the relevant tools and techniques used, fundamentals of Python and Anaconda installation, Jupyter exploration and usage, as well as data exploration with visualization using Jupyter.

Chapter 2. Data Acquisition: The chapter delves into the importance of data quality, discusses the various ways to acquire data, explains and demonstrates web scraping using different Python libraries and tools, and finally explains how data quality can be ensured.

Chapter 3. Data Cleaning and Preparation: The chapter explains the process of Data Cleaning and Preparation in detail by explaining its importance, identifying and fixing errors in the data (such as handling missing values, inconsistencies, and outliers), data transformation, data integration, and some libraries dedicated to data cleaning.

Chapter 4. Exploratory Data Analysis: The chapter discusses Exploratory Data Analysis, emphasizing its importance and the steps involved in the process. It covers various exploration methods, including descriptive statistics, correlation analysis, and dimensionality reduction. Additionally, it explores various visualizations, cluster analysis, and some Auto-EDA low-code libraries, as well as provides real-life use case explanations to help readers understand how to approach a problem and try to solve it.

Chapter 5. **Statistical Analysis**: The chapter helps you understand Statistical analysis, its importance, and the steps involved in the process. It demonstrates various statistical methods and techniques such as descriptive statistics, probability distributions, and statistical tests using real data. Additionally, it covers various libraries for statistical analysis and helps understand the determination of relationships between variables.

Chapter 6. **Time Series Analysis and Forecasting**: The chapter equips you with the knowledge of time series analysis and forecasting and its importance. It discusses various topics such as seasonality, trend, noise, auto-correlation, partial auto-correlation, white noise, and visualization. The chapter demonstrates different time series algorithms like simple moving average, exponential smoothing, Auto-regressive, and ARIMA using a real dataset. It also explores how parameters of created models and performance metrics are determined, and finally discusses some auto time series libraries.

Chapter 7. **Signal Processing**: The chapter demonstrates the importance of Signal Processing and understanding audio data, including sampling rate, amplitude, bit depth, waveform, and spectrogram. It covers various audio signal processing techniques and demonstrates the use of Python libraries for performing these techniques, as well as for speech recognition and transcription.

Chapter 8. **Analyzing Real-World Data Sets using Python**: The chapter guides you in understanding real-world datasets, their characteristics, techniques to handle the datasets, in-depth data analysis, and statistical analysis of a real-world dataset using Python. It also discusses other low-code and no-code tools such as Julius, Gigasheet, Mito, PivotTableJs, Drawdata, PyGWalker, and so on.

Appendix A Python Cheat Sheet: The chapter illustrates the Python programming language in the form of a cheat sheet that will give you an advantage while trying to solve data analysis, data cleaning, and data visualization problems. It covers various Python basics such as datatypes, commenting techniques, syntax and keywords, various operators, control structures like loops and conditional statements, data structures like lists, sets, dictionaries, and tuples, building functions, the anonymous lambda function, Object-Oriented Programming System (OOPS), and exceptions.

This book is a hands-on guide filled with practical examples, real-world scenarios, and various no-code and low-code tools that will improve efficiency and reduce work hours when building projects. I hope this journey through Data Analysis and Cleaning using Python and other tools helps you to build the best Data Analysis applications along with improving your programming skills. Happy coding!

Downloading the code bundles and colored images

Please follow the links or scan the QR codes to download the
Code Bundles and Images of the book:

https://github.com/OrangeAVA/Ultimate-Python-Libraries-for-Data-Analysis-and-Visualization

The code bundles and images of the book are also hosted on
https://rebrand.ly/gqfkrhd

In case there's an update to the code, it will be updated on the existing
GitHub repository.

Errata

We take immense pride in our work at **Orange Education Pvt Ltd,** and follow best practices to ensure the accuracy of our content to provide an indulging reading experience to our subscribers. Our readers are our mirrors, and we use their inputs to reflect and improve upon human errors, if any, that may have occurred during the publishing processes involved. To let us maintain the quality and help us reach out to any readers who might be having difficulties due to any unforeseen errors, please write to us at :

errata@orangeava.com

Your support, suggestions, and feedback are highly appreciated.

DID YOU KNOW

Did you know that Orange Education Pvt Ltd offers eBook versions of every book published, with PDF and ePub files available? You can upgrade to the eBook version at **www.orangeava.com** and as a print book customer, you are entitled to a discount on the eBook copy. Get in touch with us at: **info@orangeava.com** for more details.

At **www.orangeava.com**, you can also read a collection of free technical articles, sign up for a range of free newsletters, and receive exclusive discounts and offers on AVA™ Books and eBooks.

PIRACY

If you come across any illegal copies of our works in any form on the internet, we would be grateful if you would provide us with the location address or website name. Please contact us at **info@orangeava.com** with a link to the material.

ARE YOU INTERESTED IN AUTHORING WITH US?

If there is a topic that you have expertise in, and you are interested in either writing or contributing to a book, please write to us at **business@orangeava.com**. We are on a journey to help developers and tech professionals to gain insights on the present technological advancements and innovations happening across the globe and build a community that believes Knowledge is best acquired by sharing and learning with others. Please reach out to us to learn what our audience demands and how you can be part of this educational reform. We also welcome ideas from tech experts and help them build learning and development content for their domains.

REVIEWS

Please leave a review. Once you have read and used this book, why not leave a review on the site that you purchased it from? Potential readers can then see and use your unbiased opinion to make purchase decisions. We at Orange Education would love to know what you think about our products, and our authors can learn from your feedback. Thank you!

For more information about Orange Education, please visit **www.orangeava.com**.

Table of Contents

1. **Introduction to Data Analysis and Data Visualization using Python**............ 1

    Introduction..1

    Structure...2

    Defining Data Analysis...2

    The Importance of Data Analysis...2

    The Role of Data Analysis in Decision-Making...3

        Types of Data Analysis and their Application in Decision-Making 4

    Key Steps in the Data Analysis Process...4

        Tools and Techniques Used in Data Analysis..5

    Understanding Data Visualization...5

        Importance of Data Visualization 5

        Principles of Effective Data Visualization 6

    The Basics of Data Visualization 7

        Choosing the Right Visualization 7

    Python and Anaconda Installation 7

        Anaconda installation..8

    Data Exploration and Analysis...9

    Conclusion..20

    Keywords 20

2. **Data Acquisition** 21

    Introduction..21

    Structure...21

    Importance of Data Quality 22

    Different Ways to Acquire Data 22

        Collecting Data from Surveys...22

        Scraping Data from Websites 23

        Using APIs to Acquire Data..23

    Libraries used for Web Scraping...23

        Web Scraping Tools created using Beautiful Soup and Selenium 24

Accessing data using dedicated libraries and API 39

Ensuring Data Quality 43

Conclusion.. 44

    Keywords 44

3. Data Cleaning and Preparation **45**

Introduction.. 45

Structure.. 45

Introduction to Data Cleaning and Preparation 46

    Importance of Data Cleaning and Preparation 46

Identifying and Fixing Errors in Data 46

    Data Validation 47

    Handling Missing Values 47

    Handling Inconsistencies and Outliers 51

Data Transformation... 56

    Creating New Variables 56

    Standardization 59

    Normalization.. 59

    Standardization versus Normalization 60

    Feature Engineering Techniques 60

    Log Transform 60

    Square Root Transform.. 62

Data Integration 64

    Concatenation 64

    Merge... 66

    Join 68

Bonus Libraries for Data Cleaning... 68

    Pyjanitor 68

    Ftfy 69

    Polars... 69

Ensuring Data Consistency and Comparability 69

    Data Consistency.. 70

    Data Comparability 70

Conclusion.. 70
4. Exploratory Data Analysis **72**
Introduction... 72
Structure.. 72
Introduction to Exploratory Data Analysis (EDA)..................... 73
    Importance of EDA 73
    The whole EDA Process 73
Data Analysis Methods for Exploration...................................... 74
    Descriptive Statistics...74
    Data Distribution Analysis 76
    Histogram 77
    KDE Plot..77
    ECDF plot 78
    QQ plot..79
    Correlation Analysis 79
    Spearman Correlation 82
    Dimensionality Reduction 83
Visualizations for Exploring Data 85
    Univariate Analysis 86
    Bivariate Analysis.. 87
    Multivariate Analysis.. 88
Identifying Patterns and Trends 89
    Cluster Analysis 89
Auto EDA tools (pandas profiling and D-tale) 91
    D-tale 91
    Pandas-profiling... 96
Case Studies... 98
    EDA on a Retail Sales Dataset 99
    EDA on a Healthcare Dataset... 99
    EDA on Finance Dataset.. 99
    EDA on Manufacturing Dataset.. 100

Conclusion..100

    Future directions in exploratory data analysis.................................101

Keywords 101

5. Statistical Analysis **102**

Introduction..102

Structure..102

Introduction to Statistical Analysis...103

    Importance of Statistical Analysis 103

Statistical Analysis Workflow...103

    Data Exploration 104

    Variable Selection..104

    Statistical Tests 104

    Interpretation of Results 104

    Reporting and Visualization 104

Statistical Methods and Techniques..105

    Descriptive Statistics..108

    Probability Distributions 116

    Statistical Tests 122

    Hypothesis Testing 124

Libraries for Statistical Analysis..130

Determining Relationships between Variables 132

Making Predictions about Future Events 132

Conclusion...133

References 134

Keywords 134

6. Time Series Analysis and Forecasting **135**

Introduction...135

Structure..135

Understanding Time Series Analysis and Forecasting..............136

Importance of Time Series Analysis and Forecasting 137

Time Series Analysis 137

    Types of Time Series Data 137

Stationarity and Non-Stationarity...139

Trend, Seasonality, and Noise 141

Autocorrelation and Partial Autocorrelation.........................146

Autocorrelation 146

Partial Autocorrelation...147

White Noise 148

Visualizing Time Series Data...149

Time Series Forecasting...151

Simple moving average...151

Exponential Smoothing 152

Autoregressive (AR) 154

ARIMA 156

FbProphet 164

Deep Learning for Time Series Forecasting (CNN and LSTM)...........164

Evaluation of Time Series Forecasting Models 165

Exploring the Parameters in the Time Series Models............165

Performance Metrics of the Models to Measure their Accuracy 166

Auto Time Series Libraries 167

Conclusion.. 169

References..170

Keywords 170

7. **Signal Processing** **171**

Introduction...171

Structure...171

Introduction to Signal Processing..172

Brief Overview of Signal Processing and its
Importance in Data Analysis 172

Introduction to Audio Signal processing and its Applications............ 174

Understanding Audio Data...175

Audio Data 176

Introduction to Python Libraries for Audio Data Processing 177

Audio Signal Processing Techniques 183

Introduction to Various Audio Signal Processing Techniques............183

Use of Python for Implementing these Techniques 185

Speech Recognition and Transcription... 188

Techniques used in Speech Recognition and Transcription 188

Walkthrough of a Python Code Example for Speech Recognition and Transcription...189

Conclusion... 192

8. **Analyzing Real-World Data Sets using Python** **193**

Introduction... 193

Structure.. 194

An Overview: Using Python to Analyze Real World Projects................. 194

Understanding Real-World Data Sets.. 195

Characteristics of Real-World Data Sets.................................196

Handling Complexities in Real-world Data Sets.....................197

Exploratory Data Analysis and Visualization using Python 198

Introduction to Julius 208

Overview of Julius as an AI Tool..208

Exploratory Data Analysis and Visualization using Julius 210

Data Analysis Using No-code or Low-code Tools................................214

Gigasheet..215

Mito..215

PivotTableJS.. 217

Drawdata 217

PyGWalker 218

Visual Python..219

Conclusion...220

APPENDIX A Python Cheat Sheet..**221**

Introduction..221

Structure..222

Python Basics...222

Control Structures 224

While loop... 225

For loop 225

Control Statements 225

Data Structures 227

List 228

Tuple 230

Dictionaries 230

Sets 233

Functions 235

Defining functions 235

Lambda Anonymous Function 236

Built-in functions 237

Object Oriented Programming System 237

Defining classes, creating objects, instance variables, and methods 237

Exceptions 239

Defining exceptions, handling exceptions using try, except, and finally 239

Conclusion 240

References 241

Index **242**

## CHAPTER 1

Introduction to Data Analysis and Data Visualization using Python

Introduction

Data analysis and visualization are the most essential skills in the AI era that are being used by each individual and organization for greater profitability. With the advent of open-source programming languages like Python, and R and various libraries like Pandas, NumPy, Matplotlib, Seaborn, and so on, data analysis and visualization operations have reached the public. Anyone these days can learn to code using Python and excel in their careers. This chapter, "*Introduction to Data Analysis and Data Visualization Using Python*", explains the concept of data analysis, its importance, its role in decision-making, the various tools and techniques involved, the importance of data visualization, the best practices of data visualization, python and anaconda installation, and a use case to approach a real-life data analysis problem.

Structure

In this chapter, we will discuss the following topics:

- Defining Data Analysis
- The Importance of Data Analysis
- The Role of Data Analysis in Decision-Making
- Key Steps in the Data Analysis Process
- Understanding Data Visualization
    - The Importance of Data Visualization
    - Principles of Effective Data Visualization
- Python and Anaconda Installation
- Data Exploration and Analysis

Defining Data Analysis

Exploring, manipulating, and modeling data is the process of obtaining pertinent information and aiding in decision-making. Information from the data is extracted using statistical methods and other analytical approaches. Data analysis examines the data to discover patterns, trends, and insights for more intelligent and informed decision-making. Understanding and utilizing what, where, when, and how of the business allows businesses to operate better. The stakeholders would be able to make data-driven decisions to maximize revenue and compete in the market. The Data analysis stakeholders are from a wide range of industries, including technology, healthcare, sports, finance, marketing, sales, human resources, and defense, to mention a few.

The Importance of Data Analysis

Data analysis is the most important technique to make informed decisions, be it for individual stakeholders, multinational companies, students, researchers, or anyone who is dealing with data daily. It helps gain valuable insights and patterns from complex, large, static, or dynamic data. A good-quality data analysis operation helps uncover hidden trends and patterns in the data, understand opportunities, and reduce risks for running smooth businesses. It is more of a data-driven, objective, and evidence-based approach over intuitive approaches, which used to happen a few decades ago. A lot of companies are turning to data analysis these days since they already have been sitting on terabytes or petabytes of data without leveraging it. They had the resources in terms of talent, profit, and hardware, but could not understand what was going wrong in terms of their performance metrics, so they have been investing heavily in data analysis and related techniques to improve their value in the market. Moreover, with the advent of high-speed internet, lowering hardware costs, and a lot of research and development in the computer science and algorithms field, there are even more avenues to exploit data to improve profits. Without data analysis, there are considerable risks of wrong decision-making and, ultimately, failure.

The Role of Data Analysis in Decision-Making

Data analysis helps in informed decision-making across all sectors presently. At the core, data analysis helps convert raw, messy data into actionable insights to make informed decisions. Data analysis can support companies in exploring new market opportunities, enhancing operational flexibility, and boosting profitability. By identifying areas of need and creating interventions that are tailored to specific requirements, data analysis can also assist the public sector in enhancing the delivery of public services, thus improving public life, increasing the standard of living, and boosting a country's economy. Because of this, decision-makers should comprehend the significance of data analysis to make wise choices that can improve outcomes for all stakeholders.

Challenges of Data Analysis and Strategies for Overcoming Them

The large amount of data available for analysis can be overwhelming when it comes to handling, and if not managed well, can lead to bad decision-making. The data should be complete and accurate for analysis. So, the problem at hand should be defined very well beforehand, for example, what questions are we trying to answer, what are the gaps that need to be filled while working with the data, who are the final stakeholders, and are they looking in the right direction to get their problems solved. These critical questions need answers, then only the process of data collection and data analysis should be done. The data should also be collected from the right sources to avoid any mishap in terms of the accuracy or cleanliness of the data. Next, the data analysts must use the right analytical tools and techniques to answer the questions the stakeholders are looking for. This way the problems will be solved, and all necessary questions will be answered.

Types of Data Analysis and their Application in Decision-Making

Various types of data analysis are used, namely, **descriptive analysis, predictive analysis, and prescriptive analysis**. The **descriptive analysis** provides insights into the frequency distribution, central tendency, and data dispersion. This helps in highlighting hidden patterns and trends in the data which helps expert stakeholders understand complex datasets, for example, exploring multiple lung X-ray image datasets to understand whether a patient is likely to have lung cancer or not, based on the descriptive analysis results. The doctors who are the stakeholders here can take help from the data analysts and their results to optimize their diagnosis procedures. **Predictive analysis** helps forecast or predict future trends. Statistical tests and correlations are used to perform predictive analysis on the datasets. With the X-ray image example previously, machine learning algorithms can be trained on a dataset of X-ray images of patients with and without lung cancer to develop a predictive model that can accurately predict the presence of lung cancer in patients. **Prescriptive Analysis** is the recommendation that doctors can give to patients who are suffering from lung cancer. They can come up with customized treatment plans for each patient based on the stage of lung cancer and other parameters that the descriptive analysis provided before. These are examples that are given to demonstrate the concept of descriptive, predictive, and prescriptive analysis in real-life scenarios. Of course, things are more complicated than the examples provided.

Key Steps in the Data Analysis Process

The data analysis process involves several key steps, which are as follows:

- **Data collection:** It involves gathering pertinent information from a variety of sources, including databases, APIs, spreadsheets, surveys, and open-source data websites, to mention a few. To collect the data, web scraping is an option.
- **Data Cleaning and Preparation:** The method for addressing missing values, and eliminating duplicates, handling outliers, and converting data into an analysis-ready format.
- **Data exploration:** It is the process of examining a dataset using descriptive statistics, visualization, and summary to gain an understanding and spot underlying patterns.
- **Data modeling and analysis:** Using various statistical approaches such as correlations, t-tests, z-tests, machine learning algorithms, and other

mathematical models to extract detailed information about the dataset and provide answers to some crucial issues for the stakeholders.

- **Data Visualization:** Plots, graphs, charts, heatmaps, and other visual representations of the data are used to effectively communicate insights to stakeholders and to create narratives for dashboards. This approach makes it easier to communicate the facts about the data. An in-depth discussion is given for the following section of data visualization.

Tools and Techniques Used in Data Analysis

The tools and techniques used in data analysis are numerous. Programming is primarily done in languages like R and Python. However, there are additional programming languages like MATLAB, Scala, and Octave that are used too. To understand more intricate patterns, trends, and relationships in the dataset, there are numerous **statistical approaches, such as correlations, and numerous tests, such as t-tests, z-tests, hypothesis testing**, and so on, that are used to perform data analysis in detail. Additionally, there are various **graphs, maps, charts, and plots** to visually portray the results and provide a better explanation and representation of the data. Furthermore, the final findings are predicted and classified using machine learning algorithms, data mining, and predictive modeling techniques. There are also a lot of other good techniques to assist the decision-makers in solving problems. Although, it is up to the data analysts and data scientists to solve the problems using the right tools and techniques. If the questions are answered rightfully, then everyone is happy, be it the client, the data analyst, the private enterprise, or any public organization.

Understanding Data Visualization

The depiction of data using visual components including graphs, maps, charts, plots, heatmaps, and infographics is known as data visualization. It is a potent method that aids in making difficult knowledge more comprehensible and approachable. Data visualization makes it simple to spot patterns, trends, and linkages, which improves comprehension and decision-making.

Importance of Data Visualization

Data visualization is one of the most important techniques while doing data analysis since it is like a bridge between the client and the data analyst. Some of the reasons for using data visualization are:

- **Simplifies Complexity:** Visualizations simplify the datasets' complexity and make it simpler to understand the underlying patterns and trends in the data,

- **Enhances Decision-Making:** Visualizations make it possible for decision-makers to comprehend information and reach conclusions more quickly than ever,

- **Reveals Insights and Patterns:** Data visualizations help in identifying hidden trends, patterns, and correlations that may not be easily detectable by rudimentary data exploration,

- **Supports Storytelling:** Visualizations are best for storytelling where data analysts can present their findings more interactively and succinctly to the clients,

- **Facilitates Data Exploration:** Data Visualization helps to explore the data in a back-and-forth manner after the data analysts have some results, this way they can go back to the data and dig deeper to understand the complicated intricacies which were not possible before,

- **Improves Data Communication:** If created well, the data visualization can talk a lot to even nontechnical audiences in a sound manner, the dashboard with charts, and plots, if represented in the right way can do wonders for the team and the project,

Principles of Effective Data Visualization

To create effective visualizations, it is important to follow certain principles:

- **Clarity:** Visualizations should convey the results clearly without any confusion or blurriness.

- **Simplicity:** If the visual representation is kept simple without any jargon, that itself will answer a lot of questions.

- **Relevance:** The visuals should answer the right questions for the right audience and everything will be fine.

- **Accuracy:** The visualizations should be accurate to represent the relevant data and not some other datasets.

- **Consistency:** To tell a story, the plots, maps, charts, and graphs, should maintain a consistent flow to build a synchronized narrative for the client or stakeholder, or else a lot can be lost in explaining the images themselves.

- **Interactivity:** The visualizations if made interactive can enable the users to play with them, for example, give a slider to check the changes in the graph, introduce a dropdown for various categories, and so on.

- **Contextualization:** Include legends for categories, colors for different elements, and annotations to give context for a better understanding of the data.

The Basics of Data Visualization

There are some basics of data visualization as follows:

Choosing the Right Visualization

There are various visualization charts, plots, graphs, and maps that have different purposes of representation. So, it is better to select the right plot for the correct visual storytelling. Some of the common visualizations are as follows:

- **Bar Charts:** Bar charts show the frequency or distribution of categories and are used to compare categorical data. They work well for making comparisons between several categories or groups.
- **Line Charts:** Line charts are used to demonstrate trends and alterations across time. They work well for displaying continuous data that has a distinct temporal or sequential order.
- **Pie Charts:** Pie charts are used to display how something is made up as a whole. They can be used to show the percentages and proportions of various categories within a dataset.
- **Scatter Plots:** Scatter plots are used to show how two continuous variables relate to one another. They aid in finding outliers, correlations, and patterns in the data.
- **Histograms:** Histograms are used to show how a continuous data set is distributed. They display the data points' frequency inside predetermined bins or intervals.
- **Heatmaps:** Heatmaps are used to visualize data tables or matrixes. They use color gradients to represent values, which makes it simpler to spot patterns or connections between variables.

Python and Anaconda Installation

Python is the most popular programming language that is being used for Data Analysis and Machine Learning. Although other languages like R, Scala, MATLAB, and Octave are also used, Python is an open-source programming language, easier to learn, has a vast community of contributors, and a lot of other useful libraries make it the favorite for a beginner as well as an advanced level programmer. **Anaconda** is a free distribution of Python that includes popular data analysis packages like **pandas, NumPy, matplotlib, seaborn, SciPy, Plotly,**

and so on. Here, the installation of Python will be covered along with installing Anaconda, creating the environment, and using the relevant commands to set up the environment from scratch.

Anaconda installation

Installing Anaconda is the first step in setting up the environment for performing data analysis. Before that, let's understand why Anaconda is better and more flexible to set up. Anaconda is easy to set up and install, and it also has its GUI interface called Anaconda Navigator, which helps beginners to start crunching data and making visuals. Secondly, Anaconda provides a package management tool named **conda**, which makes it easier to install, update, and manage packages. It also helps to create environments separately for different projects. This way multiple versions of Python and libraries can be installed inside isolated environments without interfering with each other. Lastly, there are pre-installed packages like scikit-learn, pandas, NumPy, Plotly, seaborn, Matplotlib, SciPy, and so on, which make the data science task even more seamless and flexible to work with.

Steps of Anaconda Installation:

1. Go to the **Anaconda website** and download the software

2. Double-click the downloaded file

3. Follow the instructions to finish the installation process

4. Open `Anaconda prompt` by going to `Start> Programs > Anaconda3(64-bit)> Anaconda Prompt`

5. Next, type the following one after the other in the prompt to verify whether Python and Anaconda are installed

   ```
   python -version
   conda -version
   ```

If you find that the versions can be seen, then both Python and Anaconda are installed successfully.

Next, let's set up an environment by using the following steps:

Using Commands to Set up the Environment

1. Type the following in the Anaconda prompt:

   ```
   conda create --name myenv python=3.9 pandas numpy matplotlib scipy
   plotly seaborn
   ```

This will create a new environment named **myenv** with **Python 3.9** version, and install the packages **pandas, numpy, matplotlib, scipy, plotly, and seaborn**.

2. Now that **myenv** environment is created, let's activate it by typing the following command:

```
conda activate myenv
```

The `myenv` environment is activated now.

3. Then we can type **Jupyter notebook** to open the browser so that we can start solving our data analysis problems. The next section is a use case for getting into the world of data exploration and analysis.

Data Exploration and Analysis

The objective of this use case is to explain the **basic functions, libraries, and other tools** relevant to data exploration and analysis. Also, some explanations of the Jupyter Notebook are put together for better clarity. Here is a dataset of the **ball-by-ball record of the IPL (Indian Premier League)** starting from **2008 till 2022**. 2023 results are not included in the dataset. Some preliminary analysis is being shown to understand the step-by-step process.

After the Jupyter is running on the browser, it will look something as shown in *Figure 1.1*:

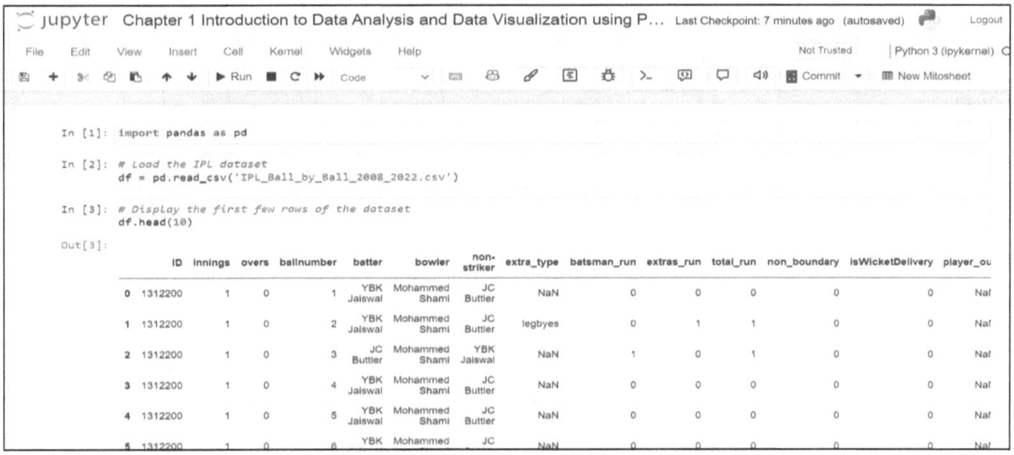

Figure 1.1: *Jupyter Notebook representation*

There are various fields at the top like **File**, **Edit**, **View**, **Insert**, **Cell**, **Kernel**, **Widgets**, and **Help**. These have their functionalities when it comes to the usage of the Jupyter Notebook.

Once the **File** option is clicked, it looks as shown in *Figure 1.2*:

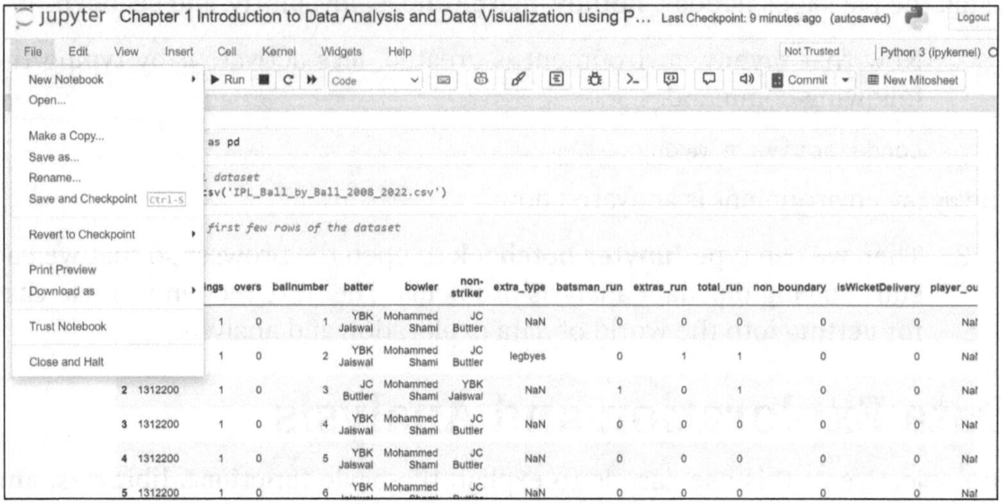

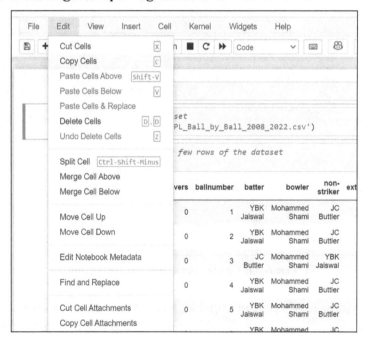

Figure 1.2: *File option representation when clicked*

There are options like creating a new notebook, opening an existing notebook, saving, downloading, renaming, reverting to a particular timestamp checkpoint, and so on. This option provides us with the facility of handling the notebook correctly and creating and opening notebooks.

Figure 1.3: *Edit option representation when clicked*

The **Edit** option as the name suggests helps in copying, pasting, and deleting cells. The cells are the individual boxes where the codes are written. The cells can also be shifted up or down as per the requirement. The next option is the **View** option.

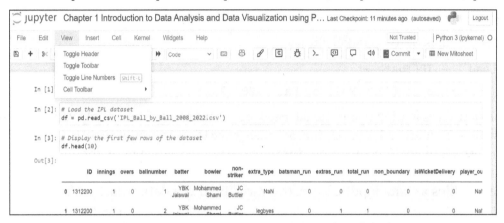

Figure 1.4: *View option representation when clicked*

Clicking the Toggle Header will remove the header (Jupyter Data Analysis and Data Visualization code) and re-clicking it will bring it back. Clicking the Toggle Toolbar will keep or remove the options bar of **File**, **Edit**, **View**, **Insert**, and so on.

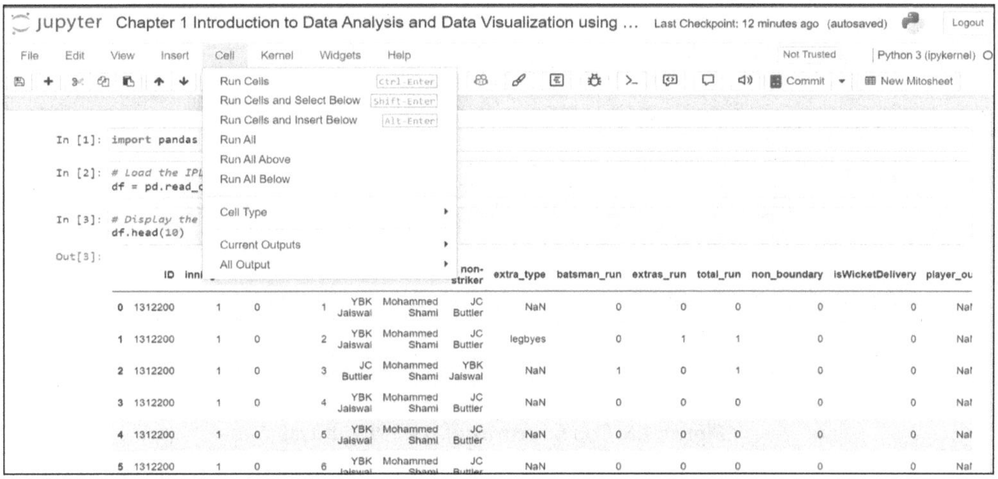

Figure 1.5: *Cell option representation when clicked*

The **Insert** option will either **Insert a cell above or below**. The **Cell** option will **Run All** cells, or one cell, or **Run All Above**, or **Run All Below**, and so on. These are the few options that you can explore while programming in Python on a Jupyter Notebook. You can also **install the R programming language** on Jupyter to perform data analysis operations.

To start with the data analysis operations, let's import the installed packages like pandas, numpy, matplotlib, and seaborn. The installation was done earlier using **conda** where multiple packages were installed.

```
import pandas as pd
```

pd is the alias of the pandas library

```
# Load the IPL dataset
df = pd.read_csv('IPL_Ball_by_Ball_2008_2022.csv')
```

The dataset is loaded using the **pd.read_csv()** function. This is only valid to load .csv files. To load a .xlsx or .xls file, **pd.read_excel()** is the right function. Datasets can also be in .html, .json, or .xls formats so that we can change the functions as per the requirement. Primarily in this exercise or in the next chapters, we will use .csv files as data inputs. Here, the variable **df is a data frame** which is a data set format in pandas. A **data frame is a data structure** that is handled by the **pandas library in Python**. It is a **2D table format** with **rows and columns** exactly like **Excel or Google Sheets**. Some of the most common methods to handle data frames are as follows.

```
# Display the first few rows of the dataset
df.head()
```

Figure 1.6: *Top 5 records of the IPL dataset*

From **df.head()** we get the top 5 rows of the data frame df. For the bottom 5, **df.tail()** is used. If we want the top 10 records, **df.head(10)** is used.

```
df.head(10)
```

Out[7]:

	ID	innings	overs	ballnumber	batter	bowler	non-striker	extra_type	batsman_run	extras_run	total_run	non_boundary	isWicketDelivery	player_ou
0	1312200	1	0	1	YBK Jaiswal	Mohammed Shami	JC Buttler	NaN	0	0	0	0	0	Na
1	1312200	1	0	2	YBK Jaiswal	Mohammed Shami	JC Buttler	legbyes	0	1	1	0	0	Na
2	1312200	1	0	3	JC Buttler	Mohammed Shami	YBK Jaiswal	NaN	1	0	1	0	0	Na
3	1312200	1	0	4	YBK Jaiswal	Mohammed Shami	JC Buttler	NaN	0	0	0	0	0	Na
4	1312200	1	0	5	YBK Jaiswal	Mohammed Shami	JC Buttler	NaN	0	0	0	0	0	Na
5	1312200	1	0	6	YBK Jaiswal	Mohammed Shami	JC Buttler	NaN	0	0	0	0	0	Na
6	1312200	1	1	1	JC Buttler	Yash Dayal	YBK Jaiswal	NaN	0	0	0	0	0	Na
7	1312200	1	1	2	JC Buttler	Yash Dayal	YBK Jaiswal	NaN	0	0	0	0	0	Na
8	1312200	1	1	3	JC Buttler	Yash Dayal	YBK Jaiswal	NaN	4	0	4	0	0	Na
9	1312200	1	1	4	JC Buttler	Yash Dayal	YBK Jaiswal	NaN	0	0	0	0	0	Na

Figure 1.7: *Top 10 records of the IPL dataset*

```
df.columns
```

```
Index([‘ID’, ‘innings’, ‘overs’, ‘ballnumber’, ‘batter’, ‘bowler’,
‘non-striker’, ‘extra_type’, ‘batsman_run’, ‘extras_run’, ‘total_
run’, ‘non_boundary’, ‘isWicketDelivery’, ‘player_out’, ‘kind’,’
fielders_involved’, ‘BattingTeam’],
dtype=’object’)
```

`df.columns` give the list of columns in the data frame. Here, all the relevant columns are found starting from innings to overs to ball number to the batter to **`batsman_run`** to **`extras_run`** and so on. The column names seem relevant for now. But if needed, we can rename them later. Next, let's check out the number of rows and columns present in the data frame.

```
num_rows, num_cols = df.shape
print(“Number of rows:”, num_rows)
print(“Number of columns:”, num_cols)
```

Output:

```
Number of rows: 225954
Number of columns: 17
```

We just see that there are **17** columns and **225954 rows**, each row corresponding to each bowl bowled in each match. So, if we consider 1 season, and there are 40 matches in total, and each match has **240 bowls bowled (6*20* 2 innings meaning 6 bowls in each over and 20 overs total)**, we should have **9600 bowls** in the whole tournament. Of course, we are not considering the extra bowls and also the IPL rules and format have changed over time. The numbers will always vary.

```
data_types = df.dtypes
print(data_types)
```

Output:

```
In [7]: data_types = df.dtypes
        print(data_types)
        ID                  int64
        innings             int64
        overs               int64
        ballnumber          int64
        batter              object
        bowler              object
        non-striker         object
        extra_type          object
        batsman_run         int64
        extras_run          int64
        total_run           int64
        non_boundary        int64
        isWicketDelivery    int64
        player_out          object
        kind                object
        fielders_involved   object
        BattingTeam         object
        dtype: object
```

Figure 1.8: *List of datatypes of all the variables in the IPL data frame*

The datatypes of the **attributes (the columns or features that make up the data frame)** as shown in the figure are **mostly integers and some are object (string datatypes)** types like fielders involved, **batter**, **bowler**, **non-striker**, **extra_type**, and so on.

The **extra_type** object feature has categories, such as wide, leg bye, no ball, bye, and so on. Next, let's check out the number of missing values in each attribute. These are data types that are here by default, later the datatypes may need to be changed for the right analysis of the dataset.

```
missing_values = df.isnull().sum()
print(missing_values)
```

```
In [8]:  missing_values = df.isnull().sum()
         print(missing_values)

         ID                       0
         innings                  0
         overs                    0
         ballnumber               0
         batter                   0
         bowler                   0
         non-striker              0
         extra_type          213905
         batsman_run              0
         extras_run               0
         total_run                0
         non_boundary             0
         isWicketDelivery         0
         player_out          214803
         kind                214803
         fielders_involved   217966
         BattingTeam              0
         dtype: int64
```

Figure 1.9: *Number of missing values for each variable*

Most of the missing values are in the variables **extra_type**, **player_out**, **kind**, and **fielders_involved**.

Next is the descriptive statistics of the data frame.

`df.describe()`

In [12]:	df.describe()								
Out[12]:		ID	innings	overs	ballnumber	batsman_run	extras_run	total_run	non_boundary	isWicketDelivery
	count	2.259540e+05	225954.000000	225954.000000	225954.000000	225954.000000	225954.000000	225954.00000	225954.000000	225954.000000
	mean	8.320470e+05	1.483868	9.185679	3.619750	1.243523	0.066907	1.31043	0.000093	0.049351
	std	3.379542e+05	0.503104	5.681797	1.810633	1.618166	0.341470	1.60605	0.009640	0.216600
	min	3.359820e+05	1.000000	0.000000	1.000000	0.000000	0.000000	0.00000	0.000000	0.000000
	25%	5.012620e+05	1.000000	4.000000	2.000000	0.000000	0.000000	0.00000	0.000000	0.000000
	50%	8.297370e+05	1.000000	9.000000	4.000000	1.000000	0.000000	1.00000	0.000000	0.000000
	75%	1.178395e+06	2.000000	14.000000	5.000000	1.000000	0.000000	1.00000	0.000000	0.000000
	max	1.312200e+06	6.000000	19.000000	10.000000	6.000000	7.000000	7.00000	1.000000	1.000000

Figure 1.10: *Descriptive Statistics of each numerical variable*

`df.describe()` gives us the descriptive statistics for the numerical variables in the dataset. The ID column can be ignored since it does not provide any value. We will delete it in the next section. The **overs**, **ballnumber**, **batsman_run**, **extras_run**, **total_run** columns does give us a lot of information. The average number of runs scored by batsmen is 1.24 per ball and the maximum is 6, since 6 is the maximum run that can be scored by the bat by playing 1 ball. **Total_run** is 1.31 per ball. **IsWicketdelivery** is either the ball was a wicket ball or a non-wicket ball meaning whether the bowler was able to take a wicket in that ball or not (if yes, it's a 1 otherwise it's a 0). It's a binary variable.

```
df['non_boundary'].value_counts()
```

Output:

```
0       225933

1          21
```

Most runs are scored by boundaries, as can be seen, in **225933** records or balls where a boundary was hit (either 4 or 6). Obviously, in T20s majority of the runs scored are by boundaries be it 4s or 6s.

```
df['isWicketDelivery'].value_counts()
```

Output:

```
0       214803

1        11151
```

Most of the balls are non-wicket balls for obvious reasons since if the majority of balls are wicket balls, there would be a minimal number of runs scored. In the preceding two code snippets, **.value_counts()** gives the number of records for each category. **df['isWicketDelivery'].value_counts()** means how many balls are without wicket balls and how many are wicket balls.

The preceding code snippets are the data exploration and analysis that we did. In the next chapters, a deep dive into various functions of pandas, numpy, scipy, plotly, matplotlib will be used to demonstrate more effective techniques of data exploration, analysis, and visualization. Some visualization codes are as follows:

```
import matplotlib.pyplot as plt
# Filter data for player scores
player_scores = df['batsman_run']
# Plot histogram
plt.hist(player_scores, bins=20, edgecolor='black')
plt.xlabel('Player Scores')
plt.ylabel('Frequency')
plt.title('Distribution of Player Scores')
plt.show()
```

Output:

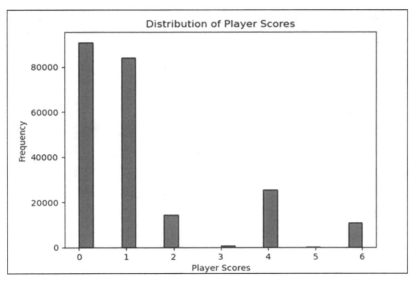

Figure 1.11: *Distribution of runs scored by players*

Matplotlib library is a data visualization library in Python and is used in this code to find the **frequency bins** of each run scored by batsmen. Here maximum runs scored were 0s means most balls were dots (no runs scored), then single runs were scored, then 2 runs and 3 runs were less since in T20s the batsmen don't run a lot anyway. Boundaries (4s and 6s) are a lot in number since for 20 overs every team wants to score maximum runs in minimum time. The plot is a **histogram plot. Xlabel shows the Player scores in the x-axis, ylabel is the Frequency in the y-axis, and title is the Distribution of Player scores**.

The next code snippet is the **demonstration of maximum aggregate run scorers in IPL** using the Seaborn library.

```
import seaborn as sns
# Group data by batsman and calculate total runs
batsman_runs = df.groupby('batter')['batsman_run'].sum().reset_index()
# Sort data by total runs
batsman_runs = batsman_runs.sort_values(by='batsman_run', ascending=False).
head(10)
# Create a bar chart
plt.figure(figsize=(10, 6))
sns.barplot(x='batsman_run', y='batter', data=batsman_runs, pal-
ette='viridis')
plt.xlabel('Total Runs')
```

```
plt.ylabel('Batsman')
plt.title('Top 10 Batsmen by Total Runs')
plt.show()
```

Output:

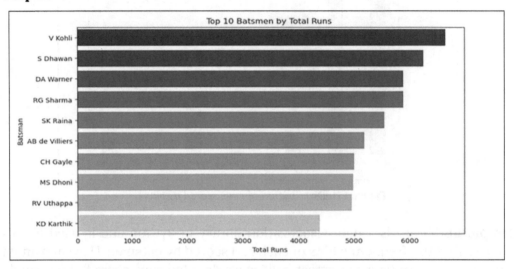

Figure 1.12: Top 10 aggregate run scorers in all the IPL matches

This code uses **.groupby()** method and the seaborn library to find the maximum run scorers over all the seasons put together. **Virat Kohli, Shikhar Dhawan, and David Warner** are the top three run scorers in the IPL seasons. Group by as the name suggests groups the data based on categories (in this case "*batter*") and calculates the sum of all the runs scored by each batsman. Then it is **sorted in descending order** by using the **.sort_values()** method (like the top 10 players in this case). Seaborn creates a horizontal bar chart to represent the **total runs on the x-axis and the players on the y-axis**. All the 9 players among the 10 players have more than 5000 runs. **Virat Kohli** being the run machine has **more than 6000 runs**. This shows that seaborn can be used to create various visualizations of various colors, textures, and types which can answer a lot of relevant business questions.

The next code answers about the type of dismissals using a pie chart. It shows the distribution of various dismissals by bowlers in the IPL.

```
dismissals = df['kind'].value_counts()
# Create a pie chart
plt.figure(figsize=(8, 8))
```

```
plt.pie(dismissals, labels=dismissals.index, autopct='%1.1f%%',
startangle=90)
```

```
plt.title('Distribution of Dismissal Types')
```

```
plt.axis('equal')
```

```
plt.show()
```

Output:

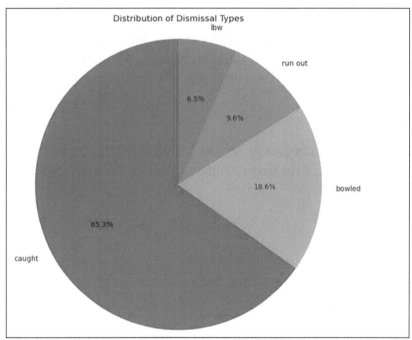

Figure 1.13: *Pie chart distribution for each dismissal type*

The **pie chart** in *Figure* 1.13 shows the kind of dismissals (caught, bowled, run out, lbw, and so on). The pie chart clearly shows that more than **65.3% of dismissals were caught, 18.6% were bowled, 9.6% were run out, and 6.5% were lbw**. This says a lot about the game format. It's a T20 game, so it's obvious the batsmen are going to hit from ball one, and they get caught too. Of course, they score too. Bowlers bowl well, and the batsman gets bowled out, meaning the batsman is not defending but going all out to score as many runs as possible. The code uses the `.pie()` method to create the pie chart. The main idea of the data analysis use case here was not only to scratch the surface of the methodology to follow for the data analysis process but also to connect how this analysis can be used to answer real-life questions about the problem, for example, how the batsmen are performing against certain bowlers, only 4s and 6s contribute to the bulk of the runs scored, caught outs are the most common dismissals, and so on.

Conclusion

This chapter covered the basics of data analysis, its importance, the significance of decision-making concerning data analysis, the tools and technologies used for performing data analysis, the steps of data analysis, data visualization, and its importance, the principles of effective data visualization, explanation of various charts and maps, Python and Anaconda installation, setting up of environments, walkthrough of how Anaconda Jupyter can be used, and a stepping stone to the world of data analysis, exploration, and visualization. In the next chapter, more in-depth and specific topics on Pandas, NumPy, Matplotlib, Seaborn, SciPy, Bokeh, statsmodels, and so on will be explored.

Keywords

Data Analysis, Data Visualization, Python, Anaconda, Jupyter Notebook, Data Analysis real use cases, data frame, Pandas, NumPy, Matplotlib, pie charts, bar chart, histogram

CHAPTER 2

Data Acquisition

Introduction

Data acquisition is the process of data collection from different sources. The data can be collected from normal government websites, open-source sites like **NASA**, **World Bank, United Nations, worldometer,** and so on, using various APIs like **IMDB, Mercedez Benz, Cricinfo,** and so on, also from sites like Wikipedia, Twitter, Amazon, eBay, and acquiring data from survey sites like SurveyMonkey. There are also tons of websites across all verticals like these that help in data acquisition for data analysis and data science projects. In this chapter, we will go through the process of exploring various websites to acquire data for analysis or just for understanding the process of web scraping using various libraries like `beautiful soup, requests, Scrapy, selenium, pandas.read_html()`, to name a few.

Structure

In this chapter, we will discuss the following topics:

- Importance of Data Quality
- Different ways to acquire data
    - Collecting Data from Surveys
    - Scraping Data from Websites
    - Using APIs to Acquire Data
- Accessing data using dedicated libraries and APIs
- Ensuring Data Quality

Importance of Data Quality

The **data quality** is the most important factor when it comes to foolproof analysis and the right decision-making. Bad data not only skews the results but also undermines the whole purpose of solving the problem of data analysis and data modeling for predictions. Any high-quality data should be **accurate, complete, consistent, and timebound**, that is, should have temporal data when needed to track the changes in the data over time. This will help in producing actionable insights and maintaining the credibility of the data and the analyst using it.

Different Ways to Acquire Data

There are various ways of acquiring data, starting from **collecting data from surveys, scraping data with websites, and accessing data from APIs** (Application Programming Interfaces).

Collecting Data from Surveys

Surveys are created by various websites these days, like **SurveyMonkey, Google Forms, Qualtrics, Typeforms, Qualtrics**, and so on. These surveys are filled up by various people, depending on the objective of the survey. These are sets of multiple-choice questions or simply providing answers based on likelihood (the higher the number between 1 and 10, the more likely it is). Of course, the surveys are targeted towards a specific audience for high-quality responses. So, the collected survey data can be accessed in various formats, like spreadsheets, or databases for further analyses. These kinds of acquired data can help understand what real-life datasets can be like. For example, it is very common for university students to prepare a questionnaire and share it among his/her colleagues for a survey that is part of a big project. For example, there is a project to analyze how playing sports just before exam day can hamper test results. The acquired data in the form of spreadsheets can help understand how many students play sports before the exam day and yet score good results. On the other hand, another category can be students who do not play and yet cannot score well on test results. **Various factors can be brought in to create the questions to deduce how can sports affect one's test results positively or negatively.** This was just a very simple example to explain the whole concept of acquiring data from survey results.

Scraping Data from Websites

Web scraping is used to extract data from websites automatically using certain libraries like `Beautiful Soup, Selenium, Scrapy,` and so on. The Python codes which are written using the preceding libraries help to skim through web pages, specifically identify the right data, and extract it in a structured format like **text, json type data, tabular-based data**, and so on. For example, we can access news sites like **CNBC, BBC, NDTV, Times of India,** and so on for specific news articles daily and just read that news according to our requirements. It is a very handy automation tool when it comes to acquiring tabular data like **Amazon reviews data, product detail data, or even data from Wikipedia like the percentage of economic growth of nations over the last 10 years.** This can be helpful to forecast results for the coming years. Also, during the pandemic, researchers acquired COVID data from various sites to carry out beautiful analyses and visualizations that solved problems like the spread of COVID over a geographical area, which factors contributed more to the spread of the disease, and how it affected people over various demographic factors like age, location, gender identity, weather conditions, and so on.

Using APIs to Acquire Data

Data from many websites and services can be accessed and extracted via APIs (Application Programming Interfaces). The extracted data is often presented in a key value (.json file format) or a tabular format. Real-time data access, authentication, and data consistency are made possible with the use of APIs. The developer automates the process of data acquisition using various tools, be it coding tools or noncoding tools. For example, the data is accessed and obtained for later use using the `requests` library in Python. However, it is imperative to understand that the number of requests the developer makes can be blocked after a certain limit of requests is crossed.

Libraries used for Web Scraping

Some of the libraries used for web scraping are `Beautiful Soup, Scrapy,` **and** `Selenium`. Moreover, we will also demonstrate the usage of **pandas** methods like `pandas.read_html()` to extract data from websites. Beautiful Soup is an easy-to-use library to extract **HTML and XML elements**. However, it is slow to use for **larger and more complex websites** where **Selenium** comes into play. **Selenium** is more of a web automation tool that can scrape dynamically generated websites or websites that require user interaction. However, it is very complicated to use as compared to `Beautiful Soup. Scrapy.` On the other hand, it is less complex to use than Selenium but more complex to use than Beautiful Soup. **Requests** is another library **used for making HTTP requests**. It is used for websites that require authentication or special headers.

Note *intended to the readers: For chapter 2 specifically, we have extracted GDP per capita data, population data, run margins data, AQI data, luxury good price data, and so on. We executed the code and extracted the data around 6 to 7 months back. The numbers were different then, and when we run the code now, the numbers are different, so please be aware of this fact.*

Web Scraping Tools created using `Beautiful Soup` and **Selenium**

This section will address the usage of Beautiful Soup to acquire data from various websites be it **tabular data, key-value format (.json) data, or text-based data**. In the first example, we will look at this website **https://worldpopulationreview. com/country-rankings/gdp-per-capita-by-country** to extract the **Highest GDP (Gross Domestic Product) per Capita** values and the **Lowest GDP per Capita** values calculated in US Dollars. The code is as follows:

```python
from bs4 import BeautifulSoup

import requests

import json


# Send a GET request to the target URL

response = requests.get('https://worldpopulationreview.com/country-
rankings/gdp-per-capita-by-country')

# Create a BeautifulSoup object to parse the HTML content

soup = BeautifulSoup(response.content, 'html.parser')


# Locate the table elements

tables = soup.find_all('table')


# Function to extract data from a table

def extract_table_data(table):
    headers = [header.text for header in table.select('tr:nth-of-type(1)
    th')]
```

```
    data_rows = table.select('tr:nth-of-type(n+2)')
    data = []

    for row in data_rows:
        row_data = [cell.text for cell in row.select('td')]
        row_dict = {headers[i]: row_data[i] for i in range(len(headers))}
        data.append(row_dict)

    return data


# Scrape the data from the tables
output = {
    "Top 10 Countries with the Highest GDP per Capita (US Dollars)":
extract_table_data(tables[0]),
    "10 Countries with the Lowest GDP per Capita in the World (US
Dollars)": extract_table_data(tables[1]),
}


# Print the extracted data as JSON
print(json.dumps(output, indent=2))
```

Code Explanation:

The **BeautifulSoup** library extracts data out of HTML and XML files, **requests** library is used for making HTTP requests, **json library** is used for **working with JSON data**. The **.get request** retrieves the HTML content of the website. The code then creates a **BeautifulSoup object** to **parse the HTML content**. This allows the code to **extract data from the HTML content**. Then the table elements are located on the website. The two tables need to be extracted from the website, one for the **top 10 countries with the highest GDP per capita** and one for the **top 10 countries with the lowest GDP per capita**. The following figure shows the tabular format of the countries with the highest GDP per capita.

Largest victories							
Winner	Margin	Target	Overs	Opposition	Ground	Match Date	Scorecard
India	317 runs	391	22.0	v Sri Lanka	Thiruvananthapuram	15 Jan 2023	ODI # 4505
Australia	309 runs	400	21.0	v Netherlands	Delhi	25 Oct 2023	ODI # 4681
Zimbabwe	304 runs	409	25.1	v U.S.A.	Harare	26 Jun 2023	ODI # 4601
India	302 runs	358	19.4	v Sri Lanka	Wankhede	2 Nov 2023	ODI # 4690
New Zealand	290 runs	403	28.4	v Ireland	Aberdeen	1 Jul 2008	ODI # 2727
Australia	275 runs	418	37.3	v Afghanistan	Perth	4 Mar 2015	ODI # 3623
South Africa	272 runs	400	29.0	v Zimbabwe	Benoni	22 Oct 2010	ODI # 3061
South Africa	258 runs	302	20.1	v Sri Lanka	Paarl	11 Jan 2012	ODI # 3225
India	257 runs	414	43.1	v Bermuda	Port of Spain	19 Mar 2007	ODI # 2542

Figure 2.1: *The Highest GDP per capita and the table element where each row is present (for example, the first row has Monaco with the highest GDP per capita, then Liechtenstein, and so on)*

The code defines the function **extract_table_data()**. The function takes a table element as input and returns a list of dictionaries. Each dictionary in the list represents a row in the table. The dictionary contains the **data from the row**, such as the **country name, the GDP per capita, and the rank**.

The code then calls the **extract_table_data()** function for each of the tables on the website. This extracts the data from the tables and stores it in a list of dictionaries. The dictionary named **output** is created. The dictionary **contains two tables.** The keys of the dictionary are the **names of the tables**, and the values of the dictionary are **the list of dictionaries** that contain **the data from the table**.

Then the final data is **extracted in a JSON format**. The data looks as in *Figure 2.2:*

```
{
    "Top 10 Countries with the Highest GDP per Capita (US Dollars)": [
        {
            "Rank": "1",
            "Country/Territory": "Monaco",
            "GDP per Capita (US$)": "234,317"
        },
        {
            "Rank": "2",
            "Country/Territory": "Liechtenstein",
            "GDP per Capita (US$)": "169,260"
        },
        {
            "Rank": "3",
            "Country/Territory": "Luxembourg",
            "GDP per Capita (US$)": "133,175"
        },
        {
            "Rank": "4",
```

Figure 2.2: *The list of dictionaries inside a main JSON file which shows the Highest GDP per capita results*

The following diagram is the **list of dictionaries** containing the details of the nations with the **lowest GDP per capita** as extracted from the website:

```
            {
                "Rank": "10",
                "Country/Territory": "Denmark",
                "GDP per Capita (US$)": "68,037"
            }
        ],
        "10 Countries with the Lowest GDP per Capita in the World (US Dollars)": [
            {
                "Rank": "1",
                "Country/Territory": "Yemen",
                "GDP per Capita (US$)": "302"
            },
            {
                "Rank": "2",
                "Country/Territory": "Burundi",
                "GDP per Capita (US$)": "311"
            },
            {
                "Rank": "3",
                "Country/Territory": "Afghanistan"
```

Figure 2.3: *The second dictionary inside the main JSON
file showing the nations with the Lowest GDP per capita*

In the next example, we will extract text-based data from a news article using Beautiful Soup from the website **https://www.cnbctv18.com/business/ vedanta-will-be-a-trillion-dollar-company-in-next-10-years-says-anil- agarwal-16819691.htm.**

The article has the **article title, the date, the time stamp, and the content of the article**. These are the main points we will extract from the CNBC article. Let's check the following code:

```python
import requests
from bs4 import BeautifulSoup


url = "https://www.cnbctv18.com/business/vedanta-will-be-a-trillion-dollar-company-in-next-10-years-says-anil-agarwal-16819691.htm"


# Send a request to the website
response = requests.get(url)


# Parse the HTML code
soup = BeautifulSoup(response.content, "html.parser")
```

```
# Find the text that you want to extract
articles = soup.find("div", class_=["jsx-1801027680 new-article",
"jsx-1801027680 art-page-wrapper"])


# Iterate through all the articles and extract the text
for article in articles:
    text = article.text



# Print the text
print(text)
```

Code Explanation:

This code is used to extract the text from a website. The code first imports the **requests** and **BeautifulSoup** libraries. These libraries are used to **send a request** to the website and **parse the HTML code**. Then the **.get()** method is used to extract the **HTML content** of the website like before. This time it's not table data, but text data. The code then parses the HTML code using the **BeautifulSoup** library. The soup variable is a **BeautifulSoup** object that contains the parsed HTML code.

The code then finds the text that you want to extract using the **find()** method. The **find()** method **takes a CSS selector as input and returns the first element** that matches the selector. In this case, the CSS selector is **div**, **class_=["jsx-2597938882 nart-para", "jsx-2597938882 art-page-wrapper"]**. This **CSS selector matches** the **element that contains the text** that you want to extract.

The **CSS (Cascading Style Sheets)** selector div selects all div elements in an HTML document. The div selector is a tool for selecting elements in an HTML document. It can be used to select elements for a variety of things, like **extracting data, formatting text**, or **adding JavaScript events**.

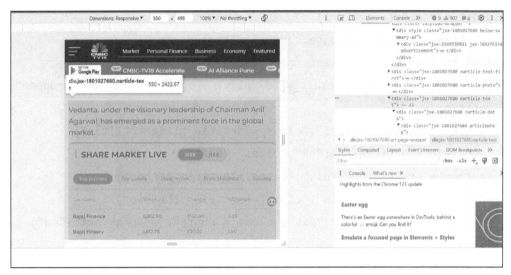

Figure 2.4: *Identifying the div element for the website to extract the text of the article*

The code then iterates through all the articles and extracts the text using the **text** property. The **text** property returns the **text content of the element**.

The final output of the text data has the **article title, the date, the time stamp,** and **the content of the article** as follows:

```
Vedanta, under the visionary leadership of Chairman Anil Agarwal, has emerged as a prominent force in the global market.Share M
arket LiveNSE Addressing the company's shareholders, Agarwal said that his ambition is to transform Vedanta into a trillion-dol
lar enterprise in the next ten years."Our vision is that Vedanta will be more than one trillion dollar company in next 10 year
s. We will produce our own copper, oil and gas," Agarwal added.According to him, innovation and developing new products are key
for growing the company.Also Read: Anil Agarwal aims to make Vedanta Resources a debt free companyHe also added that Vedanta is
the ambassador of India to the whole world.Watch video for entire conversation.First Published: May 31, 2023 6:15 PM ISTContinu
e ReadingCheck out our in-depth Market Coverage, Business News & get real-time Stock Market Updates on CNBC-TV18. Also, Watch
our channels CNBC-TV18, CNBC Awaaz and CNBC Bajar Live on-the-go!Follow us on: TagsAnil AgarwalVedantaRecommended ArticlesView
AllMahindra's aerospace arm to supply over 5,000 components for Airbus aircraft under new contractJan 17, 2024 IST2 Min ReadHap
piest Minds Q3 Results | IT company's net rises 3.5%, revenue up 12%Jan 17, 2024 IST2 Min ReadAverage number of years to become
a unicorn falls from 8.4 years in 2022 to 5.5 years in 2023Jan 17, 2024 IST3 Min ReadPersistent Systems board to consider stock
split on January 19-20Jan 17, 2024 IST2 Min Read
```

Figure 2.5: *The final text data after web scraping from the website*

The next example of **Beautiful Soup** will extract **an article from the website** `https://www.moneycontrol.com/news/business/startup/dropout-to-data-scientist-indian-firms-open-to-hiring-non-tech-candidates-with-relevant-skills-10708001.html`

The result will contain the name of the article and the content of the article.

```
import requests

from bs4 import BeautifulSoup

url = "https://www.moneycontrol.com/news/business/startup/dropout-to-
data-scientist-indian-firms-open-to-hiring-non-tech-candidates-with-
relevant-skills-10708001.html"
```

```
response = requests.get(url)
soup = BeautifulSoup(response.content, "html.parser")
# Find the text that you want to extract
article = soup.find("div", class_=["display: block;", "page_left_wrapper"])
if article:
    title = article.find("h1", class_="article_title artTitle")
    subtitle = article.find("h2", class_="article_desc")
    author = article.find("div", class_="article_author")
    date = article.find("div", class_="article_schedule")
    contents = article.find("div", class_="content_wrapper arti-flow")
    if title:
        print("Title:", title.text.strip())
    else:
        print("Title not found.")
    if author:
        print("Author:", author.text.strip())
    else:
        print("Author not found.")
    if date:
        print("Date:", date.text.strip())
    else:
        print("Date not found.")
    if contents:
        print("Contents:", contents.text.strip())
    else:
        print("Contents not found.")
else:
    print("Article not found.")
```

Code explanation:

The code first imports the **requests** library to make the **HTTP requests** and the **BeautifulSoup** library to **parse HTML content**. Next, **requests.get()** method requests to the URL, which is an article on the **moneycontrol website**. The response object is the result that has the HTML content of the article.

Next, the `BeautifulSoup` library is used to parse the **HTML content of the response object**. So, here we have the **soup** which has the HTML content of the article.

The next line of the code uses the **find()** method to find the **div** element with the class attribute `display:block` and `page_left_wrapper`. This element contains the **main content of the article**. The screenshot of the website and the HTML contents can be seen as follows:

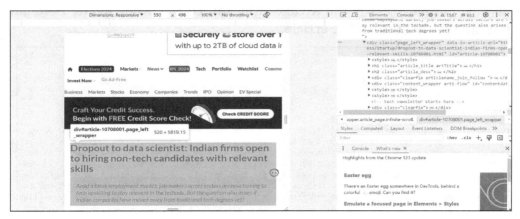

Figure 2.6: The HTML content of the webpage and the blue-colored highlighted section on the right shows the main content of the article

If the **find()** method returns a **None** value, then the article was not found. Or else, the code extracts the title of the **article, the subtitle of the article, the author, the date, and the contents of the article**.

So, to extract each variable from the website, for example, if we are extracting the title of the article, the **find()** method is used to identify the **h1 element** with the **class attribute `article_title artTitle`**. The following screenshot explains the concept.

Figure 2.7: Identifying the h1 element with the class attribute for the article title

Similarly, the other variables like the **subtitle** have the **h2 element** with the class attribute **article_desc, the author variable** has the **div** element with the class attribute **article_author**, the **date** variable has the **div** element with the class attribute **article_schedule**, the contents variable has the **div** element with the class attribute **content_wrapper arti-flow.** The text of each variable is printed into the console as shown in *Figure 2.8.*

The final output text has the **Article title, sub-title, Author name, Date and Time, and the content of the article**.

```
Title: Dropout to data scientist: Indian firms open to hiring non-tech candidates with relevant ski
lls
Sub-title: Amid a bleak employment market, job-seekers across sectors are now turning to tech upski
lling to stay relevant in the techade. But the question also arises if Indian companies have moved
away from traditional tech degrees yet?
Author: Mansi Verma
Date: Mumbai /   May 31, 2023 / 01:05 PM IST
Contents: Upskilling   At the age of 15, Prasanna Venkatesh was forced to halt his education owing
to financial constraints while his friends began their grind to get into a legacy Indian tech insti
tute.Two years later, in 2017, Venkatesh decided to pick up from where he left off. He enrolled for
a diploma in electronics and communication engineering at a polytechnic college in Chennai, his hom
etown, taking the first possible entry back into the game.Realising his diploma was not enough, Ven
katesh turned to upskilling for data science and artificial intelligence roles. "In the software in
dustry, almost everything can be learned from open source or with very little fee. If you're skille
d enough, most of the companies do not care about the degree," he told Moneycontrol.Soon, Venkatesh
landed his first internship at a startup in June 2020 earning a salary of Rs 3 lakh per annum. Duri
ng this time, he gained hands-on experience developing data science and AI solutions.Almost two yea
rs, three jobs and several experiences later, Venkatesh, today 23, earns a package of Rs 20 lakh pe
r annum, working as a data scientist and leading the machine learning team at a business solutions
```

Figure 2.8: *Final output text web scrapped from the website*

The next code is a demonstration of the **Selenium library** to extract tabular data from the website https://www.luxepolis.com/all-brands/louis-vuitton/?product_condition=2732

```python
from bs4 import BeautifulSoup

import pandas as pd

from selenium import webdriver

from selenium.webdriver.common.by import By

from selenium.webdriver.support.ui import WebDriverWait

from selenium.webdriver.support import expected_conditions as EC

from selenium.common.exceptions import TimeoutException

url = "https://www.luxepolis.com/all-brands/louis-
vuitton/?product_condition=2732"

# Set up the Selenium WebDriver

options = webdriver.ChromeOptions()

options.add_argument("--headless")
```

```
driver = webdriver.Chrome(options=options)
driver.get(url)
# Initialize the DataFrame and wait for the content to load
data = []
try:
    wait = WebDriverWait(driver, 60)  # Increase the timeout value to 60
#seconds
    wait.until(EC.presence_of_element_located((By.CSS_SELECTOR,
".product-listing")))
    # Parse the HTML content using BeautifulSoup
    soup = BeautifulSoup(driver.page_source, 'html.parser')
    # Find the elements and extract the required data
    elements = soup.select(".product-listing")
    for element in elements:
        title_element = element.select_one(".prd-brand")
        price_element = element.select_one(".price.dis-price-label")
        emi_available_element = element.select_one(".emi-avl.pull-left")
        if title_element and price_element:
            title = title_element.text.strip()
            price = price_element.text.strip()
            emi_available = bool(emi_available_element)
            data.append([title, price, emi_available])
except TimeoutException:
    print("The website took too long to load. Please try again later.")
finally:
    # Create a DataFrame and display the results
    df = pd.DataFrame(data, columns=["Product Name", "Product Price",
"EMI Available"])
    print(df)
# Close the WebDriver
    driver.quit()
```

Code explanation:

The code first imports the necessary libraries, including **BeautifulSoup, pandas, selenium,** and **WebDriverWait**. **Selenium** is a tool to automate tasks on a web browser. It can be used to **open websites, navigate through pages, and interact with elements on the page**.

Selenium opens the **Luxepolis website** and waits for the content to load. Once the content is loaded, Selenium uses the `BeautifulSoup` library to **parse the HTML content**.

The `BeautifulSoup` library extracts the **product name, product price,** and **EMI availability** from each product listing on the page.

Let's understand this section of the code.

```
# Set up the Selenium WebDriver
options = webdriver.ChromeOptions()
options.add_argument("--headless")
driver = webdriver.Chrome(options=options)
driver.get(url)
# Initialize the data frame and wait for the content to load
data = []
try:
    wait = WebDriverWait(driver, 60)  # Increase the timeout value to 60
seconds
    wait.until(EC.presence_of_element_located((By.CSS_SELECTOR, ".prod-
uct-listing")))
```

Firstly, the Selenium WebDriver is set up. The `options` parameter specifies that you want to run the **WebDriver in headless mode**. The `get()` method opens the Luxepolis website in the WebDriver.

The `wait` variable is a `WebDriverWait` object. This object allows you to wait for a certain condition to be met before continuing. In this case, the condition is that the element with the **CSS selector** `.product-listing` is present on the page. The `wait.until()` method will wait for the condition to be met for up to **60 seconds**. If the condition is not met after 60 seconds, an exception will be raised.

Next, let's understand this block of code and identify the `title`, `price`, and `EMI` **availability elements** in the website.

```
elements = soup.select(".product-listing")
for element in elements:
        title_element = element.select_one(".prd-brand")
        price_element = element.select_one(".price.dis-price-label")
```

```
emi_available_element = element.select_one(".emi-avl.pull-left")
if title_element and price_element:
    title = title_element.text.strip()
    price = price_element.text.strip()
    emi_available = bool(emi_available_element)
    data.append([title, price, emi_available])
```

The **elements** variable is a list of all the elements on the page that have the CSS selector .**product-listing**. The for loop iterates through the **elements** list and extracts the **product name,** **price,** and **EMI availability from each product listing**.

The **select_one()** method returns the first element that matches the specified selector. The **text.strip()** method **removes any whitespace** from the beginning and the end of the text. The **bool()** function converts the element to a **Boolean value**.

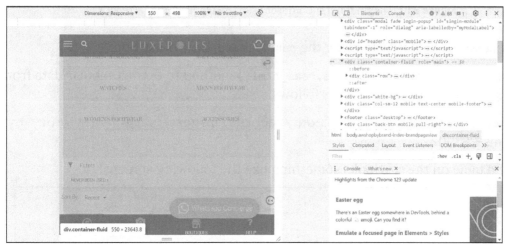

Figure 2.9: *The HTML content of the webpage and the blue-colored highlighted section on the right shows the main content of the products present on the site*

The final data is converted into a data frame format using the **pandas.DataFrame()** object. The final output data is like the following screenshot:

```
   Product Name Product Price  EMI Available
0  Louis Vuitton   INR30,000           True
1  Louis Vuitton   INR130,000          True
2  Louis Vuitton   INR135,000          True
3  Louis Vuitton   INR47,000           True
4  Louis Vuitton   INR74,000           True
5  Louis Vuitton   INR129,000          True
6  Louis Vuitton   INR122,500          True
7  Louis Vuitton   INR12,500           True
8  Louis Vuitton   INR65,000           True
9  Louis Vuitton   INR155,000          True
10 Louis Vuitton   INR230,000          True
11 Louis Vuitton   INR74,000           True
12 Louis Vuitton   INR128,000          True
13 Louis Vuitton   INR20,000           True
14 Louis Vuitton   INR30,000           True
15 Louis Vuitton   INR23,000           True
16 Louis Vuitton   INR24,000           True
17 Louis Vuitton   INR90,900           True
18 Louis Vuitton   INR143,300          True
19 Louis Vuitton   INR119,000          True
20 Louis Vuitton   INR30,800           True
21 Louis Vuitton   INR109,600          True
22 Louis Vuitton   INR38,000           True
23 Louis Vuitton   INR20,000           True
24 Louis Vuitton   INR40,000           True
25 Louis Vuitton   INR130,000          True
```

Figure 2.10: *The final output dataset as extracted from the Luxepolis dataset*

Accessing Tabular Data using the `pandas.read_html()` method.

Here, we are using the **pandas.read_html()** method to extract tabular data from the famous cricket website as follows:

https://www.espncricinfo.com/records/largest-margin-of-victory-by-runs-283902

The table on the site looks something like the following screenshot:

Largest victories							
Winner	Margin	Target	Overs	Opposition	Ground	Match Date	Scorecard
India	317 runs	391	22.0	v Sri Lanka	Thiruvananthapuram	15 Jan 2023	ODI # 4505
Australia	309 runs	400	21.0	v Netherlands	Delhi	25 Oct 2023	ODI # 4681
Zimbabwe	304 runs	409	25.1	v U.S.A.	Harare	26 Jun 2023	ODI # 4601
India	302 runs	358	19.4	v Sri Lanka	Wankhede	2 Nov 2023	ODI # 4690
New Zealand	290 runs	403	28.4	v Ireland	Aberdeen	1 Jul 2008	ODI # 2727
Australia	275 runs	418	37.3	v Afghanistan	Perth	4 Mar 2015	ODI # 3623
South Africa	272 runs	400	29.0	v Zimbabwe	Benoni	22 Oct 2010	ODI # 3061
South Africa	258 runs	302	20.1	v Sri Lanka	Paarl	11 Jan 2012	ODI # 3225
India	257 runs	414	43.1	v Bermuda	Port of Spain	19 Mar 2007	ODI # 2542
South Africa	257 runs	409	33.1	v West Indies	Sydney	27 Feb 2015	ODI # 3616
Australia	256 runs	302	14.0	v Namibia	Potchefstroom	27 Feb 2003	ODI # 1970
India	256 runs	375	36.5	v Hong Kong	Karachi	25 Jun 2008	ODI # 2716

Figure 2.11: *The website look of the dataset*

```
import requests
import pandas as pd
url = "https://www.espncricinfo.com/records/largest-margin-of-victory-
by-runs-283902"
response = requests.get(url)
df = pd.read_html(response.content)[0]
df.columns = ["Winner", "Margin", "Target", "Overs", "Opposi-
tion","Ground","Match Date","Scorecard"]
df
```

Code Explanation:

The preceding code uses the **requests library** to make the **HTTP requests** to the **Cricinfo** website. Then `pd.read_html()` method is used to **identify and read the HTML** table into a pandas data frame.

This function can be used to swiftly acquire tables from websites without figuring out how to **scrap the site's HTML contents** like the `BeautifulSoup` and **Selenium** alternatives we did before.

The final output data is shown in *Figure 2.12*. It shows the **cricket ODI match details** that have the **highest winning margins**. We can do some data analysis later using this data set obtained.

	Winner	Margin	Target	Overs	Opposition	Ground	Match Date	Scorecard
0	India	317 runs	391	22.0	v Sri Lanka	Thiruvananthapuram	15 Jan 2023	ODI # 4505
1	Australia	309 runs	400	21.0	v Netherlands	Delhi	25 Oct 2023	ODI # 4681
2	Zimbabwe	304 runs	409	25.1	v U.S.A.	Harare	26 Jun 2023	ODI # 4601
3	India	302 runs	358	19.4	v Sri Lanka	Wankhede	2 Nov 2023	ODI # 4690
4	New Zealand	290 runs	403	28.4	v Ireland	Aberdeen	1 Jul 2008	ODI # 2727
...	...	...	...	...	...	...	...	...
95	India	181 runs	312	42.3	v Namibia	Pietermaritzburg	23 Feb 2003	ODI # 1964
96	England	181 runs	369	39.0	v New Zealand	The Oval	13 Sep 2023	ODI # 4643
97	Australia	180 runs	255	27.4	v Bangladesh	Darwin	30 Aug 2008	ODI # 2758
98	Sri Lanka	180 runs	321	31.5	v South Africa	Colombo (RPS)	20 Jul 2013	ODI # 3392
99	Pakistan	180 runs	339	30.3	v India	The Oval	18 Jun 2017	ODI # 3894

100 rows × 8 columns

Figure 2.12: *The final output data frame*

Accessing population data using the `pandas.read_html()` method.

Here, we are using the **pandas.read_html()** method to extract tabular data of the population of each country in **2022 and 2023** and the **percentage change of population in the consecutive year**. The link used is

https://en.wikipedia.org/wiki/List_of_countries_by_population_(United_Nations)

The **Wikipedia data** is shown as follows:

	Country / Area	UN continental region[4]	UN statistical subregion[4]	Population (1 July 2022)	Population (1 July 2023)	Change
1	India	Asia	Southern Asia	1,417,173,173	1,428,627,663	+0.81%
2	China[a]	Asia	Eastern Asia	1,425,887,337	1,425,671,352	−0.02%
3	United States	Americas	Northern America	338,289,857	339,996,564	+0.50%
4	Indonesia	Asia	South-eastern Asia	275,501,339	277,534,123	+0.74%
5	Pakistan	Asia	Southern Asia	235,824,863	240,485,658	+1.98%
6	Nigeria	Africa	Western Africa	218,541,212	223,804,632	+2.41%
7	Brazil	Americas	South America	215,313,498	216,422,446	+0.52%
8	Bangladesh	Asia	Southern Asia	171,186,373	172,954,319	+1.03%
9	Russia	Europe	Eastern Europe	144,713,314	144,444,359	−0.19%
10	Mexico	Americas	Central America	127,504,126	128,455,567	+0.75%
11	Japan	Asia	Eastern Asia	123,951,692	123,294,513	−0.53%
12	Ethiopia	Africa	Eastern Africa	123,379,925	126,527,060	+2.55%
13	Philippines	Asia	South-eastern Asia	115,559,009	117,337,368	+1.54%
14	Egypt	Africa	Northern Africa	110,990,103	112,716,599	+1.56%

Figure 2.13: *The Wikipedia dataset*

```
import requests

import pandas as pd

url = "https://en.wikipedia.org/wiki/List_of_countries_by_population_
(United_Nations)"

response = requests.get(url)

df = pd.read_html(response.content)[0]

df.columns = ["Country/Area", "UN continental region", "UN statistical
region", "Population (1 July 2022)", "Population (1 July 2023)", "Change"]

df
```

Code explanation:

The **requests library** is used to make the **HTTP requests** to the Wikipedia site. The code pattern is **similar to the one used before in the Cricinfo site** but the most important thing is to **place the column names in the right order** as present in the Wikipedia site. The final result is the one we get as follows:

[8]:	Country/Area	UN continental region	UN statistical region	Population (1 July 2022)	Population (1 July 2023)	Change
0	World	NaN	NaN	7.975105e+09	8.095042e+09	+1.50%
1	India	Asia	Southern Asia	1.417173e+09	1.428628e+09	+0.81%
2	China[a]	Asia	Eastern Asia	1.425887e+09	1.425671e+09	−0.02%
3	United States	Americas	Northern America	3.382899e+08	3.399966e+08	+0.50%
4	Indonesia	Asia	South-eastern Asia	2.755013e+08	2.775341e+08	+0.74%
...	...	...	...	...	...	...
234	Falkland Islands (United Kingdom)	Americas	South America	3.780000e+03	3.791000e+03	+0.29%
235	Niue	Oceania	Polynesia	1.934000e+03	1.935000e+03	+0.05%
236	Tokelau (New Zealand)	Oceania	Polynesia	1.871000e+03	1.893000e+03	+1.18%
237	Vatican City[x]	Europe	Southern Europe	5.100000e+02	5.180000e+02	NaN
238	Pitcairn Islands (United Kingdom)	Oceania	Polynesia	NaN	NaN	NaN

239 rows × 6 columns

Figure 2.14: *The output data frame as extracted by the preceding code*

From *Figure 2.14*, it is seen that most of the countries in the **top 5 list experience positive population growth except China**. The continental regions like **Asia, the Americas, Oceania, Europe,** and **Africa** are also included in the data along with **the UN statistical regions**.

Accessing data using dedicated libraries and API

In this section, we will be using the **pynytimes library** to access details of books by the famous author **Mr. Stephen King**, like **book review as a link**, **date of publication, book title, book summary, author name, and the ISBN number**. The API we are using is from the **New York Times website**. So, you have to register (create an account) here **https://developer.nytimes.com/get-started** and click the new app (on the top right) using the instructions given in the preceding link. You can call the app anything, but it is better to name something relatable to the **book reviews or movie reviews.** The app you created is responsible for creating your **API key** and you **must never share it with anyone**. With that being said, let's check out the code and extract some book reviews.

```
!pip install pynytimes
```

First install the **pynytimes library** to use the API to extract the relevant data

```
from pynytimes import NYTAPI
nyt = NYTAPI("YOUR API KEY", parse_dates=True)
# Get reviews by author (first and last name)
reviews = nyt.book_reviews(author="Stephen King")
```

Code explanation:

The code is used as per the documentation of the **pynytimes library** to extract book details of the author. One can also extract **article searches, movie reviews, top stories, most viewed articles, and shared articles**. The result is as follows in the form of a list of dictionaries where **each dictionary has all the details of the book.**

Figure 2.15: *The details of the books written by Stephen King*

For example, the following dictionary in the list has the **book name Nightmares and Dreamscapes** and the other details of the **publication date, ISBN number, byline, and the review in the link**. However, the link is behind a paywall, so anyone interested can pay for a subscription and read the review.

```
{'url': 'http://www.nytimes.com/1993/10/24/books/in-short-fiction-284093.
html', 'publication_dt': datetime.date(1993, 10, 24), 'byline':
'RICHARD E. NICHOLLS', 'book_title': 'Nightmares and Dreamscapes',
```

'book_author': 'Stephen King', 'summary': '', 'uuid': '00000000-0000-0000-0000-000000000000', 'uri': 'nyt://book/00000000-0000-0000-0000-000000000000', 'isbn13': ['9781441615299']}

Accessing Stock Market data

This program is used to **scrap the stock market data of Apple** between **1st January 2020** and **31st December 2020**. For that, the **yfinance library** is installed. It is an **open-source tool** that uses **Yahoo's publicly available APIs** for **research and educational purposes**.

```
!pip install yfinance
import yfinance as yf
# Define the stock symbol and the date range
symbol = "AAPL"
start_date = "2020-01-01"
end_date = "2020-12-31"
# Fetch the historical stock data
stock_data = yf.download(symbol, start=start_date, end=end_date)
# Display the stock data
stock_data
```

Date	Open	High	Low	Close	Adj Close	Volume
2020-01-02	74.059998	75.150002	73.797501	75.087502	73.347946	135480400
2020-01-03	74.287498	75.144997	74.125000	74.357498	72.634842	146322800
2020-01-06	73.447502	74.989998	73.187500	74.949997	73.213631	118387200
2020-01-07	74.959999	75.224998	74.370003	74.597504	72.869286	108872000
2020-01-08	74.290001	76.110001	74.290001	75.797501	74.041481	132079200
...	...	...	...	...	...	...
2020-12-23	132.160004	132.429993	130.779999	130.960007	129.030823	88223700
2020-12-24	131.320007	133.460007	131.100006	131.970001	130.025909	54930100
2020-12-28	133.990005	137.339996	133.509995	136.690002	134.676407	124486200
2020-12-29	138.050003	138.789993	134.339996	134.869995	132.883194	121047300
2020-12-30	135.580002	135.990005	133.399994	133.720001	131.750122	96452100

252 rows × 6 columns

Figure 2.16: *Extracted stock market data of Apple*

There are daily data on when the stock market opens, its **highest point, its lowest point, the closing point, the adjoining closing point, and the total number of data points** for the whole day. This kind of daily data is used to test forecasting models and **predict stock market points** for the future.

Extracting Air Quality index data using API

In this section, we are extracting the **Air Quality Index (AQI)** data of various capital cities around the planet. The website https://aqicn.org/api/ is used to have the API acquired. The code first imports the **requests** library to access the HTML requests to the website. The **WAQI API** needs to be accessed to get the unique API key for each user. The **WAQI API is a free API** that provides **Air Quality data for cities worldwide.**

Next, the code defines a list of cities from around the world to fetch the AQI. Finally, the code **loops through the list of cities and acquires the AQI data for each city**. The code first constructs an API URL for each city. The API URL includes the **city name and the API key**. Then, the code makes a `requests.get()` request to the API URL. The `requests.get()` **method returns a Response object**, which contains the response from the API.

The code then parses the **response object to get the AQI data for the city**. The AQI data is stored in the **data dictionary**. If the **status** key in the data dictionary is equal to **ok,** then the code **prints the AQI for each city**. Or else, the **code prints an error message**.

```python
import requests
#https://aqicn.org/api/
#https://aqicn.org/data-platform/token/
# Replace 'YOUR_API_KEY' with the API key you received from the WAQI API
website
api_key = "YOUR_API_KEY"
# List of cities to fetch AQI data for
cities = ['New York', 'Los Angeles', 'London', 'Tokyo', 'Beijing',
"Paris", "Berlin", "Stockholm", "Warsaw", "Sofia", "New Delhi", "Dhaka",
"Bangkok"]
# Fetch AQI data for each city and display the result
for city in cities:
    api_url = f"https://api.waqi.info/feed/{city}/?token={api_key}"
    response = requests.get(api_url)
    data = response.json()
```

```
if data['status'] == 'ok':
    aqi = data['data']['aqi']
    print(f"Air Quality Index for {city}: {aqi}")
else:
    print(f"Error fetching data for {city}: {data['status']}")
```

```
Air Quality Index for New York: 21
Air Quality Index for Los Angeles: 66
Air Quality Index for London: 42
Air Quality Index for Tokyo: 22
Air Quality Index for Beijing: 53
Air Quality Index for Paris: 61
Air Quality Index for Berlin: 43
Air Quality Index for Stockholm: 22
Air Quality Index for Warsaw: 74
Air Quality Index for Sofia: 27
Air Quality Index for New Delhi: 134
Air Quality Index for Dhaka: 144
Air Quality Index for Bangkok: 65
```

Figure 2.17: *Air Quality Indexes of the major capital cities of the countries*

Ensuring Data Quality

Ensuring data quality is the process of making sure that the data is **accurate, complete, and consistent**. It will help users to understand **whether the data is fit for the purpose of analysis and modeling** in the later stages. This involves steps like **data validation, cleaning, and data transformation** which are explained as follows:

- **Data Validation and Cleaning**

  Data validation is the process of ensuring that the acquired data is **accurate, complete, and consistent** for use. It requires going through the data for **errors, missing values, duplicates, and other ambiguities**. **Data cleaning** helps in **correcting or removing errors, handling missing values, removing duplicates, and resolving inconsistencies** within the dataset. To enhance data quality before analysis, several techniques can be used, including **data profiling, outlier detection, and data imputation**. **Data verification and validation** are iterative processes that call for thorough analysis and evaluation of the collected data.

- **Data Integration and Transformation**

  Data integration involves combining data from multiple sources to create a unified dataset for analysis. **Data Transformation** is performing operations on the dataset to make it ready to be used for training machine learning models, for example, changing datatypes from string to integer whenever needed, doing normalization and standardization, and cleaning the data to get rid of anomalies, and so on.

Conclusion

This marks the end of the chapter on Data Acquisition, where we learned about various sources from where data can be collected using APIs, surveys, and various other websites. We also learned about various Python libraries which are being used to extract data from websites like `BeautifulSoup, Selenium, pandas.read_html(), requests, pynytimes, yfinance,` and so on. There are also other tools like `Scrapy, pandas.read_json()` which can be used to extract data from websites. We explored **tabular data and text-based data**. We have extracted data across all domains, starting from the **global economy, population, sports, luxury brands, books, stock market**, and some news articles, to name a few. In the next chapter, we will deep dive into the concepts of **data cleaning and preparation,** where we will explore the libraries of **pandas, numpy, pyjanitor, scipy** and use them to **fix data errors and inconsistencies, transform data suitable for analysis,** and so on. We will look into various use cases to apply and build our data from a dirty version.

Keywords

Some of the relevant keywords for the chapter are as follows:

Data Acquisition, Web scraping, python, BeautifulSoup, Requests, Selenium, Scrapy, LXML, XPATH, CSS selectors, JSON, CSV, API, MySQL

## CHAPTER 3

Data Cleaning and Preparation

Introduction

Data cleaning and preparation is the process of cleaning and transforming dirty data before going into the stage of exploratory data analysis. It is the most important step in the data science workflow which makes sure that the data is cleaned and prepared in a way for analysis and modeling in the later stages. This chapter will explain data cleaning and preparation and its importance. Next, this chapter will cover the steps of data cleaning, among which we have data validation, handling missing values, detecting outliers, and so on. After the steps of data cleaning are explained, we will deep dive into the topics of data transformation for data preparation, like standardization, normalization, and some feature engineering techniques. Next, we will understand the topics of data comparability and data consistency. For each topic, we will use Python programming language and relevant libraries like **Pandas**, **Numpy**, **Scipy**, **Pyjanitor**, **Ftfy**, and **Polars**, to name a few. We will explore the libraries and use them to **solve use cases to identify real-life problems and use cases**.

Structure

In this chapter, we will discuss the following topics:

- Introduction to Data Cleaning and Preparation
  - Importance of Data Cleaning and Preparation
- Identifying and Fixing Errors in Data
  - Data Validation
  - Handling Missing Values

- o   Handling Inconsistencies and Outliers
- Data Transformation
  - o   Creating New Variables
  - o   Standardization
  - o   Normalization
  - o   Feature Engineering Techniques
- Data Integration
  - o   Concatenation
  - o   Merge
  - o   Join
- Bonus Libraries for Data Cleaning
- Data Comparability and Data Consistency

Introduction to Data Cleaning and Preparation

Data cleaning and preparation are the fundamental steps in the data analysis process. The raw data mostly contains **errors, inconsistencies, missing values**, and other issues that can create problems concerning accurate analysis. **Data cleaning** identifies and fixes these errors, while **data preparation** focuses on transforming the data into a convenient format for analysis. The final prepared data should be **accurate, complete, consistent, and comparable**.

Importance of Data Cleaning and Preparation

Data cleaning and preparation are crucial for reliable and meaningful analysis. Bad-quality data can lead to biased or incorrect results, affecting the overall integrity and validity of the analysis. **Cleaning and preparing the data** help **eliminate errors, inconsistencies, and outliers** that may arise from data collection or storage processes. It also involves **handling missing values, ensuring data is in the correct format**, and **addressing any data quality issues**.

Identifying and Fixing Errors in Data

Identifying and fixing errors in the data is a crucial step when we are cleaning data, which helps to improve the quality of the datasets by getting rid of **duplicate, or incorrect data**. In the next sub-sections of **data validation, handling missing**

values, and handling outliers, we explore the **techniques of identifying and replacing missing values or removing missing values** completely, if needed. We will also look into various **outlier detection techniques** and experiment with them on the datasets.

Data Validation

Data validation is verifying the raw data for **errors, inconsistencies, missing values**, and **outliers**. It involves verifying that the data **follows certain rules, constraints, or predefined criteria**. Common techniques used for data validation include range checks, format checks, and consistency checks. For example, checking if **numerical data falls within expected ranges** or verifying that **dates are in the correct format** or the **datatypes in the dataset are in the right format** (for example, **string, float, integer, boolean,** and so on) or verifying **whether there are missing values in the dataset** or there are **duplicate rows in the dataset**. These are some of the data validation tests we need to perform **to identify potential errors in the dataset** while ensuring data accuracy.

Handling Missing Values

The missing values are a common issue in real-world data sets. Handling missing values is essential to **prevent biased or incomplete analysis**. Various approaches can be used to handle missing values, such as **deletion, and imputation, or advanced techniques like multiple imputation can also be used. Deletion** involves **removing rows or columns with missing values,** while **imputation** involves **estimating missing values based on patterns in the data**. The choice of approach depends on the nature of the missing data and the analysis objectives. To detect and deal with missing values, we can use some of the following techniques. The dataset is the **IPL matches dataset from 2008 to 2022.** The dataset has details of every **IPL match, starting from venue to season to match number to team name to toss decision to winning team to margin to player of the match and so on**. The data frame has **950 rows and 20 columns**. The following code is given for a demonstration.

```python
import pandas as pd
import numpy as np
import matplotlib.pyplot as plt
import seaborn as sns
# Reading a CSV file into a Pandas DataFrame
data = pd.read_csv('IPL_Matches_2008_2022.csv')
# Checking the first few rows of the DataFrame
data.head()
```

	ID	City	Date	Season	MatchNumber	Team1	Team2	Venue	TossWinner	TossDecision	SuperOver	WinningTeam
0	1312200	Ahmedabad	2022-05-29	2022	Final	Rajasthan Royals	Gujarat Titans	Narendra Modi Stadium, Ahmedabad	Rajasthan Royals	bat	N	Gujarat Titans
1	1312199	Ahmedabad	2022-05-27	2022	Qualifier 2	Royal Challengers Bangalore	Rajasthan Royals	Narendra Modi Stadium, Ahmedabad	Rajasthan Royals	field	N	Rajasthan Royals
2	1312198	Kolkata	2022-05-25	2022	Eliminator	Royal Challengers Bangalore	Lucknow Super Giants	Eden Gardens, Kolkata	Lucknow Super Giants	field	N	Royal Challengers Bangalore
3	1312197	Kolkata	2022-05-24	2022	Qualifier 1	Rajasthan Royals	Gujarat Titans	Eden Gardens, Kolkata	Gujarat Titans	field	N	Gujarat Titans

Figure 3.1: *The first five rows of the data frame*

Next, we check for the number of missing values using the following code:

```
# Check for missing values
print(data.isnull().sum())
```

The - **.isnull()** is a function that returns True/False, whether there is a null value or not and **sum()** returns total number of True values.

```
ID                 0
City               51
Date               0
Season             0
MatchNumber        0
Team1              0
Team2              0
Venue              0
TossWinner         0
TossDecision       0
SuperOver          4
WinningTeam        4
WonBy              0
Margin             18
method             931
Player_of_Match    4
Team1Players       0
Team2Players       0
Umpire1            0
Umpire2            0
dtype: int64
```

Figure 3.2: *Number of Missing values for each variable*
(the method variable has maximum missing values)

We will now impute the missing value for the `Margin` variable. We can impute using the mean or median. The `mean` is used in scenarios when the distribution is uniform (not so skewed) or there are no outliers. For cases, the `median` is used when the distribution is skewed.

We will check the **skewness of the variable**, in this case, using **a histogram**. We will also check the **skewness using the skewness function**.

```
sns.histplot(data['Margin'])
plt.show()
```

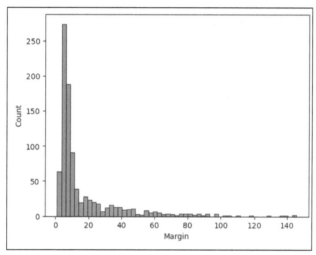

Figure 3.3: *The histogram of the Margin variable*

The preceding histogram clearly states that the **distribution is right skewed** since the data is **distributed mostly on the left and the tail is at the right**.

Next, we will check using the skewness function.

```
skewness = data['Margin'].skew()
print("Skewness:", skewness)
Output:
Skewness: 2.6535823950532107
```

The conditions for skewness are as follows:

- **Skewness** > 0: Right-skewed distribution
- **Skewness** < 0: Left-skewed distribution
- **Skewness** close to 0: Approximately symmetric distribution

The **skewness is > 0 so it is right skewed** and **in sync with the histogram result**, so we **will impute using the median.**

Now let's **impute the missing value with the** `median` for the `Margin` variable. The code is as follows:

```
# Fill missing values with the median (Imputation)
data['Margin'].fillna(data['Margin'].median(), inplace=True)  # Impute
with median

data.head()
```

The missing values are replaced by the median for the `Margin` variable. The `.fillna()` function is used to perform the operation.

	ID	City	Date	Season	MatchNumber	Team1	Team2	Venue	TossWinner	TossDecision	SuperOver	WinningTeam	WonBy	Margir
0	1312200	Ahmedabad	2022-05-29	2022	Final	Rajasthan Royals	Gujarat Titans	Narendra Modi Stadium, Ahmedabad	Rajasthan Royals	bat	N	Gujarat Titans	Wickets	7.(
1	1312199	Ahmedabad	2022-05-27	2022	Qualifier 2	Royal Challengers Bangalore	Rajasthan Royals	Narendra Modi Stadium, Ahmedabad	Rajasthan Royals	field	N	Rajasthan Royals	Wickets	7.(
2	1312198	Kolkata	2022-05-25	2022	Eliminator	Royal Challengers Bangalore	Lucknow Super Giants	Eden Gardens, Kolkata	Lucknow Super Giants	field	N	Royal Challengers Bangalore	Runs	14.(
3	1312197	Kolkata	2022-05-24	2022	Qualifier 1	Rajasthan Royals	Gujarat Titans	Eden Gardens, Kolkata	Gujarat Titans	field	N	Gujarat Titans	Wickets	7.(
4	1304116	Mumbai	2022-05-22	2022	70	Sunrisers Hyderabad	Punjab Kings	Wankhede Stadium, Mumbai	Sunrisers Hyderabad	bat	N	Punjab Kings	Wickets	5.(

Figure 3.4: *The missing values are replaced in the Margin variable*

We will drop the method variable **since it has 931 entries missing from 950 entries**. We won't touch the other variables because **we may lose important information**.

All the rows can be deleted too if there are most missing values like the `method` variable.

```
# Drop missing values
data_drop = data.dropna(subset= ['method'])

data_drop.head()
```

This can be done using the `.dropna()` method. It will delete all the rows which have even one cell missing.

hNumber	Team1	Team2	Venue	TossWinner	TossDecision	SuperOver	WinningTeam	WonBy	Margin	method	Player_of_Match	Team1Players	T
32	Delhi Daredevils	Rajasthan Royals	Arun Jaitley Stadium	Rajasthan Royals	field	N	Delhi Daredevils	Runs	4.0	D/L	RR Pant	['PP Shaw', 'C Munro', 'SS Iyer', 'RR Pant', '...	
18	Kolkata Knight Riders	Kings XI Punjab	Eden Gardens	Kings XI Punjab	field	N	Kings XI Punjab	Wickets	9.0	D/L	KL Rahul	['CA Lynn', 'SP Narine', 'RV Uthappa', 'N Rana...	
6	Rajasthan Royals	Delhi Daredevils	Sawai Mansingh Stadium	Delhi Daredevils	field	N	Rajasthan Royals	Runs	10.0	D/L	SV Samson	['AM Rahane', 'DJM Short', 'BA Stokes', 'SV Sa...	
Eliminator	Sunrisers Hyderabad	Kolkata Knight Riders	M Chinnaswamy Stadium	Kolkata Knight Riders	field	N	Kolkata Knight Riders	Wickets	7.0	D/L	NM Coulter-Nile	['DA Warner', 'S Dhawan', 'KS Williamson', 'Yu...	
50	Royal Challengers Bangalore	Kings XI Punjab	M Chinnaswamy Stadium	Kings XI Punjab	field	N	Royal Challengers Bangalore	Runs	82.0	D/L	V Kohli	['CH Gayle', 'V Kohli', 'AB de Villiers', 'KL ...	

Figure 3.5: *Deleting all the rows where maximum rows have missing values*

The resulting data frame has all the columns (only with the margin column with no missing values).

Handling Inconsistencies and Outliers

Data entry mistakes, measurement mistakes, and system flaws are a few examples that might cause inconsistent or incorrect data to appear. Typically, **numerical outliers** are those that **deviate from the mean by more than three standard deviations**. Maintaining data integrity requires spotting and managing anomalies and discrepancies.

Techniques such as **data profiling, data visualization, and statistical methods** can be employed to **detect inconsistencies and outliers**. One of them is visual identification where we plot the data and simply look for the data points that are different from the rest of the data, for example, using box plots we can identify the outliers. Here, the **box plots** are used to find how the data is distributed from **minimum to maximum range**. It also gives us information on the `mean`, `median` **(50th percentile), 25th percentile,** and **75th percentile**.

```
#Outlier detection using box plot
# Plot the box plot
sns.boxplot(data['Margin'])
```

Here, we are using the Seaborn library for using the boxplot. The `Margin` variable is being used in this case to showcase in the boxplot and identify the outliers.

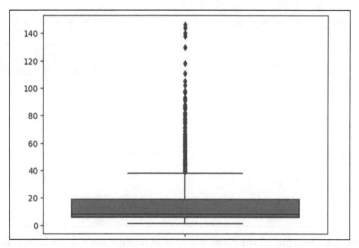

Figure 3.6: *Boxplot showing the range of Margin values in the IPL dataset*

From *Figure* 3.6, it can be observed that most of the **Margin** results range from 0 to 40, where 40 is the maximum value and 0 is the minimum value. **75%** of the data is below **18** (approximate value) and **25%** of the data is **below 5** (approximate value). The maximum run margin is **40**. And if we observe more there are numbers ranging from 40 to 140. The numbers that are **more than 120 are outliers** since they **do not correlate** with the **minimum to maximum range numbers**.

Inter-Quartile Range (IQR) Technique

The next technique that is used frequently to detect and handle outliers is the **Inter-Quartile Range (IQR)** technique. This technique identifies **outliers by comparing a data point to the IQR**. The IQR is the difference between the **75th and 25th percentiles** of a distribution. Outliers are typically defined as data points that are **less than the 25th percentile - 1.5 * IQR** or **greater than the 75th percentile + 1.5 * IQR**.

```
#Outlier detection
#IQR Technique
# Plot the distribution of the 'Margin' column
plt.hist(data['Margin'])
plt.xlabel("Margin")
plt.ylabel("Frequency")
plt.title("Distribution of Margin Values")
plt.show()
# Identify outliers using the Interquartile Range (IQR)
```

```
Q1 = data['Margin'].quantile(0.25)
Q3 = data['Margin'].quantile(0.75)
IQR = Q3 - Q1
# Define outliers as values outside the 1.5 IQR range
outliers = data[data['Margin'] < Q1 - 1.5 * IQR]
outliers = pd.concat([outliers,(data[data['Margin'] > Q3 + 1.5 * IQR])])
# Print the outliers
outliers
```

The preceding code calculates the **Inter Quartile Range** using the **1st and the 3rd Quartile (the 25th and the 75th percentile values)**. Then the outliers are calculated based on the (**Q1-1.5*IQR and Q3+1.5*IQR values**). Here **Q1 is the 25th percentile** and **Q3 is the 75th percentile**. We also have a **histogram** plotted which gives us an idea of the **distribution of the data**. The majority of the data is **concentrated between 0 and 60 runs**. The outliers lie after 120–140.

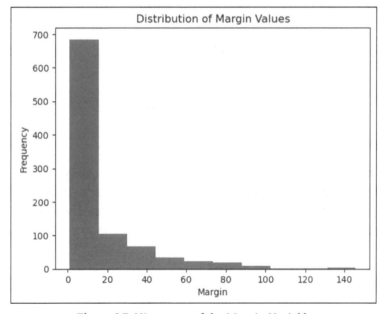

Figure 3.7: *Histogram of the Margin Variable*

The following screenshot shows the **detected outliers in the Margin variable** in the data frame. It follows the formula from (**Q1-1.5*IQ and Q3+1.5*IQR** values) above.

WinningTeam	WonBy	Margin
Kolkata Knight Riders	Runs	54.0
Punjab Kings	Runs	54.0
Gujarat Titans	Runs	62.0
Kolkata Knight Riders	Runs	52.0
Chennai Super Kings	Runs	91.0

Figure 3.8: *Outliers in the data frame*

Z-Score Technique

A statistical technique called the **z-score outlier detection technique** employs the standard deviation to find outliers. The **z-score** is determined by **first subtracting the mean from each data point and then dividing the result by the standard deviation**. A **z-score** of three or above is typically regarded as an anomaly.

```
import numpy as np

# Calculate the z-scores

z_scores = np.abs(data['Margin'] - data['Margin'].mean()) / data['Margin'].std()

# Define outliers as data points that are more than 3 standard deviations
away from the mean

outliers = z_scores[z_scores > 3]

Outliers
```

The **z-score technique** in the preceding code uses the **(x-μ)/sigma** formula from statistics. Here, **sigma is the standard deviation, μ is the mean, and x is a data point**. The following screenshot shows the set of data points that are the detected outliers using the **z-score technique**. The **1st column** is the **index number of the data frame** and the **2nd column** gives us the number which has a value > 3 for detecting the outlier.

```
19       3.418054
80       3.186927
147      3.279378
166      3.002025
188      3.695407
242      4.666141
273      3.926534
329      5.960453
346      3.002025
364      3.695407
383      3.002025
388      5.868002
396      3.140701
453      5.590650
468      3.695407
544      3.510505
597      5.220846
604      3.186927
605      3.233152
629      3.186927
709      3.002025
713      4.342563
729      3.140701
826      3.741632
877      3.464279
887      3.464279
894      4.065210
949      5.683101
Name: Margin, dtype: float64
```

Figure 3.9: *Outlier detection using the z-score technique*

```
data.iloc[list(outliers.index)]
```

We will see the data frame with the indices that has the outliers using the preceding code.

ID		City	Date	Season	MatchNumber	Team1	Team2	Venue	TossWinner	TossDecision	SuperOver	WinningTeam	Wo
19	1304101	Navi Mumbai	2022-05-08	2022	55	Chennai Super Kings	Delhi Capitals	Dr DY Patil Sports Academy, Mumbai	Delhi Capitals	field	N	Chennai Super Kings	F
80	1254106	Sharjah	2021-10-07	2021	54	Kolkata Knight Riders	Rajasthan Royals	Sharjah Cricket Stadium	Rajasthan Royals	field	N	Kolkata Knight Riders	
147	1216524	NaN	2020-10-27	2020/21	47	Sunrisers Hyderabad	Delhi Capitals	Dubai International Cricket Stadium	Delhi Capitals	field	N	Sunrisers Hyderabad	F
166	1216540	NaN	2020-10-12	2020/21	28	Royal Challengers Bangalore	Kolkata Knight Riders	Sharjah Cricket Stadium	Royal Challengers Bangalore	bat	N	Royal Challengers Bangalore	F

Figure 3.10: *The Outliers with the indices*

There are also other outlier detection techniques like **Tukey's fences** which is similar to the IQR technique but uses different thresholds to define outliers. **Tukey's fences** define **1.5*IQR for the lower outliers and 3*IQR for the upper outliers**. There are also some machine learning outlier detection methods like **Isolation Forest and the local outlier factor**.

Data Transformation

Data Transformation is used to change the scale or distribution of the variables or convert one datatype to another. Here, **numerical variables** can be **transformed to reduce the skewness by taking the logarithm**. A **categorical variable** can be converted to a **dummy variable**. New variables can also be created for convenience when needed. The techniques of **standardization and normalization** are also used for data transformation to convert the data to a suitable scale for processing.

Creating New Variables

Creating new variables is needed to understand the data well and introduce fresh functions from the existing ones. They help in solving problems related to data cleaning as well as analysis. The following example code helps us understand the creation of new variables. The data is an **insurance dataset** that has the variables of **age, sex, BMI, number of children, smoker(yes/no), region, and charges**.

```
# Reading a CSV file into a Pandas DataFrame
data = pd.read_csv('insurance.csv')


# Checking the first few rows of the DataFrame
data.head()
```

The data frame looks something like the following screenshot:

	age	sex	bmi	children	smoker	region	charges
0	19	female	27.900	0	yes	southwest	16884.92400
1	18	male	33.770	1	no	southeast	1725.55230
2	28	male	33.000	3	no	southeast	4449.46200
3	33	male	22.705	0	no	northwest	21984.47061
4	32	male	28.880	0	no	northwest	3866.85520

Figure 3.11: *Insurance data frame*

Let's say we want to create a new column.

```
# Applying a function to a column
data['new_charges'] = data['charges'].apply(lambda x: x * 2)
data['new_charges']
```

It creates a new column by **squaring the charges variable** and creating a new variable known as **new_charges** using the **lambda function** inside the data frame and then using the **.apply()** function.

The new data frame has the **new_charges** variable, as shown in *Figure 3.12*:

	age	sex	bmi	children	smoker	region	charges	new_charges
0	19	female	27.900	0	yes	southwest	16884.92400	33769.84800
1	18	male	33.770	1	no	southeast	1725.55230	3451.10460
2	28	male	33.000	3	no	southeast	4449.46200	8898.92400
3	33	male	22.705	0	no	northwest	21984.47061	43968.94122
4	32	male	28.880	0	no	northwest	3866.85520	7733.71040

Figure 3.12: *Dataframe after the new_charges variable is created*

We can also use the binning technique to categorize the ages into different categories like **Young**, **Adult**, and **Senior.**

```
# Create a new feature called 'AgeGroup'
data['AgeGroup'] = data['age'].apply(lambda x: 'Young' if x < 30 else
'Adult' if x < 50 else 'Senior')
```

The newly created data frame is as follows:

	age	sex	bmi	children	smoker	region	charges	new_charges	AgeGroup
0	19	female	27.900	0	yes	southwest	16884.92400	33769.84800	Young
1	18	male	33.770	1	no	southeast	1725.55230	3451.10460	Young
2	28	male	33.000	3	no	southeast	4449.46200	8898.92400	Young
3	33	male	22.705	0	no	northwest	21984.47061	43968.94122	Adult
4	32	male	28.880	0	no	northwest	3866.85520	7733.71040	Adult

Figure 3.13: *Dataframe after the AgeGroup variable is created*

There is this technique called **one hot encoding** which is applied to the **categorical variables to convert them into dummy variables**. Each category has its dummy variable, for example, if we want to translate **"black hair"**, then **1 for hair** and **0 for the hair color**. The numbers are just labels to identify the categories, they **do not have any ordinal relationship** like for 1 to 5-star reviews, and for a 5-star review, we will write positive words and for 1-star review, we will use not-so-positive words.

It is used mainly for machine learning modeling since they are not numerical variables and any kind of mathematical relationship cannot be found. This way the categorical variable can be identified as present or absent in the row.

```
# One-hot encode the 'Smoker' column
data = pd.get_dummies(data, columns=['smoker'], dtype = int)
```

The **.get_dummies()** function is used to convert into dummy variables.

	age	sex	bmi	children	region	charges	new_charges	AgeGroup	smoker_no	smoker_yes
0	19	female	27.900	0	southwest	16884.92400	33769.84800	Young	0	1
1	18	male	33.770	1	southeast	1725.55230	3451.10460	Young	1	0
2	28	male	33.000	3	southeast	4449.46200	8898.92400	Young	1	0
3	33	male	22.705	0	northwest	21984.47061	43968.94122	Adult	1	0
4	32	male	28.880	0	northwest	3866.85520	7733.71040	Adult	1	0
...	...	...	...	...	...	...	...	...	...	...
1333	50	male	30.970	3	northwest	10600.54830	21201.09660	Senior	1	0
1334	18	female	31.920	0	northeast	2205.98080	4411.96160	Young	1	0
1335	18	female	36.850	0	southeast	1629.83350	3259.66700	Young	1	0
1336	21	female	25.800	0	southwest	2007.94500	4015.89000	Young	1	0
1337	61	female	29.070	0	northwest	29141.36030	58282.72060	Senior	0	1

1338 rows × 10 columns

Figure 3.14: *Dummy variable represented for the smoker variable*

The **smoker variable** is a **categorical variable** with a **boolean representation as Yes or No**, so the preceding output data frame clearly shows that the new variables `smoker_yes` and `smoker_no` as **1 (wherever the person is a smoker)** and as **0 (wherever the person is a nonsmoker)**.

Standardization

Standardization (`z-score normalization`) is a technique for data transformation of the original data to the data having a **mean of 0 and a standard deviation of 1**. This happens by **subtracting the mean(µ) of the data from the data point and then dividing it by the standard deviation**. The technique is useful when the data follows the normal distribution. The following code demonstrates the concept. **Standardization** is done over the **age** variable.

```
# standardize the Series
s_standardized = (data['age'] - data['age'].mean()) / data['age'].std()
print(s_standardized)
```

The standardized data format is as follows:

```
0          -1.438227
1          -1.509401
2          -0.797655
3          -0.441782
4          -0.512957
            ...
1333        0.768185
1334       -1.509401
1335       -1.509401
1336       -1.295877
1337        1.551106
Name: age, Length: 1338, dtype: float64
```

Figure 3.15: Standardization of the age variable in the data frame

Normalization

Normalization (min-max scaling) scales the data to a fixed range (normally 0 to 1). It does this by **subtracting the minimum value of the data and then dividing the range (max-min). Normalization is better to work with** when the **data does not contain outliers** since these can skew the scaled values. The formula is like **(x-xmin)/(xmax-xmin)** where **xmax and xmin** are the maximum and minimum values of the dataset. The following code normalizes the **age** variable.

```
# normalize the Series
s_normalized = (data['age'] - data['age'].min()) / (data['age'].max() -
data['age'].min())
print(s_normalized)
```

The normalized pandas Series of the **age** variable.

```
0          0.021739
1          0.000000
2          0.217391
3          0.326087
4          0.304348
          ...
1333       0.695652
1334       0.000000
1335       0.000000
1336       0.065217
1337       0.934783
Name: age, Length: 1338, dtype: float64
```

Figure 3.16: *The normalized data*

Standardization versus Normalization

The data distribution is altered by **standardization**, having the mean at 0 and the standard deviation at 1. Standardization is useful when **you are aware that the distribution is normal**. However, it is not always mandatory. Additionally, unlike normalization, **standardization does not have a bounding range, therefore it is unaffected by outliers**.

In contrast, normalization shifts the **data's range so that it lies between 0 and 1 or -1 and +1**. The distribution of the data in this instance is unknown. Outliers impact it because of range limits like [0,1] or [-1,+1].

Feature Engineering Techniques

There are some feature engineering techniques like **log transform, square root transform, and polynomial features**. The detailed explanation of these techniques is as follows:

Log Transform

Log transform is used to deal with skewed data. It helps to handle large values, reduce skewness, and **transform the data to a more normal or Gaussian-like distribution**. The following code shows that the **charges** variable from the data frame is **right skewed,** that is, the **majority of the data is concentrated on the left side** and thus needs log transformation.

```python
import numpy as np
import matplotlib.pyplot as plt


# Perform the log transformation
data_log = np.log(data['charges'])


# Define a grid of plots
fig, axs = plt.subplots(nrows=1, ncols=2)


# Create histograms
axs[0].hist(data['charges'], edgecolor='black')
axs[1].hist(data_log, edgecolor='black')


# Add a title to each histogram
axs[0].set_title('Original Data')
axs[1].set_title('Log-Transformed Data')


# Display the plots
plt.show()
```

The **np.log()** function is used to perform the log transformation. Then a grid of plots (1 row and 2 columns) is set up using the **subplots()** function from the **matplotlib's pyplot** module. This function returns a **Figure object** and **a Numpy array** containing the created subplot Axes instances, which are stored in **fig** and **axs** respectively. **Histograms of the original** and **log-transformed data** are created using the **hist** function from the **Axes instances**. The **edgecolor** parameter is **set to 'black' to better visualize individual bins**. Then the titles are added to the histograms using the **set_title** function from the Axes instances.

Following is the set of plots where we see the **original** and the **log-transformed data**.

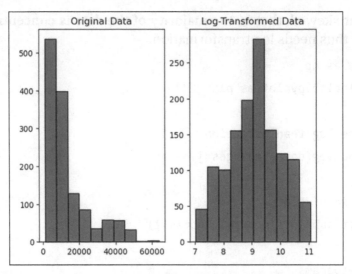

Figure 3.17: *Original and log-transformed data (charges variable)*

The preceding screenshot shows the **right-skewed data,** where the **majority of the data is concentrated on the left,** and on the right, we have the **log-transformed version, which is the normal distribution of the previous skewed data**.

Square Root Transform

The **square root transform** is a data transformation method that is used to reduce data skewness. This is specifically used when the **data is a bit skewed to the right side**.

A square root transformation involves taking the square root of each data point in the dataset. This helps reduce variance and makes the data more normally distributed. The following code shows the square root transform operation.

```
import numpy as np
import matplotlib.pyplot as plt


# Perform the square root transformation
data_sqrt = np.sqrt(data['charges'])


# Define a grid of plots
fig, axs = plt.subplots(nrows=1, ncols=2)
```

```
# Create histograms
axs[0].hist(data['charges'], edgecolor='black')
axs[1].hist(data_sqrt, edgecolor='black')

# Add a title to each histogram
axs[0].set_title('Original Data')
axs[1].set_title('Square Root Transformed Data')

# Display the plots
plt.show()
```

The preceding code structure is the same as the **log transformation** code. A few things like the **variable names and the `np.sqrt()` function name** are different.

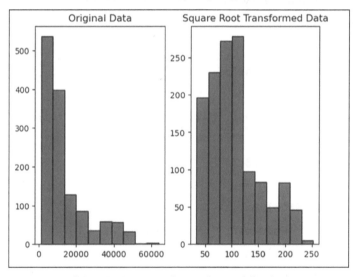

Figure 3.18: *Squared transform of the data*

The **original data is right-skewed** and the **square root transformed data is also moderately right-skewed but is nearing a normal distribution**. It is not as efficient as the log transform version since the original data is right-skewed and not left-skewed. Although, for understanding the concept it is fine to use the `.sqrt()` function in this case with the available data.

Normally, if we compare, the log transformation fares better than the square root transform. The **log transformation** can **compress high values better** than that of the square root transform. However, **Square root** can be only used for **the values >=0** while **logarithmic can't be used when values = 0**.

Data Integration

Data Integration is combining data from various sources to have a composite view of the dataset. This is often necessary during data analysis as it helps to work with the complete dataset. Various operations are used like **append, merge, join,** and **concat** to perform data integration using pandas.

Concatenation

The **concat** function in pandas is used to **concatenate rows of a data frame to the end of another data frame** thus returning a new object. If there are missing columns or rows in either data frame, then the cells are replaced by **NaN values**.

The following code explains the concept of concatenation of 2 data frames. Here, there are 3 rows each in every data frame, and the indexes are also defined.

```python
import pandas as pd


df1 = pd.DataFrame({'Column1': ['A0', 'A1', 'A2'],
                    'Column2': ['B0', 'B1', 'B2'],
                    'Column3': ['C0', 'C1', 'C2'],
                    'Column4': ['D0', 'D1', 'D2']},
                index=[0, 1, 2])


df2 = pd.DataFrame({'Column1': ['A3', 'A4', 'A5'],
                    'Column2': ['B3', 'B4', 'B5'],
                    'Column3': ['C3', 'C4', 'C5'],
                    'Column4': ['D3', 'D4', 'D5']},
                index=[3, 4, 5])


result = pd.concat([df1, df2])


result
```

The resulting data frame shows that the 2nd data frame **(df2)** is kept below the 1st data frame **(df1).**

	Column1	Column2	Column3	Column4
0	A0	B0	C0	D0
1	A1	B1	C1	D1
2	A2	B2	C2	D2
3	A3	B3	C3	D3
4	A4	B4	C4	D4
5	A5	B5	C5	D5

Figure 3.19: *Concatenated data frame*

The second code for concatenation shows missing columns in **df1**.

```
df1 = pd.DataFrame({'Column1': ['A0', 'A1', 'A2'],
                    'Column2': ['B0', 'B1', 'B2'],
                    'Column3': ['D0', 'D1', 'D2']},
                index=[0, 1, 2])


df2 = pd.DataFrame({'Column1': ['A3', 'A4', 'A5'],
                    'Column2': ['B3', 'B4', 'B5'],
                    'Column4': ['C3', 'C4', 'C5'],
                    'Column3': ['D3', 'D4', 'D5']},
                index=[3, 4, 5])


result = pd.concat([df1, df2])


result
```

The resulting data frame has **NaN values in the first 3 rows in the 4th column**.

	Column1	Column2	Column3	Column4
0	A0	B0	D0	NaN
1	A1	B1	D1	NaN
2	A2	B2	D2	NaN
3	A3	B3	D3	C3
4	A4	B4	D4	C4
5	A5	B5	D5	C5

Figure 3.20: *Concatenated data frame with NaN values*

The `concat` function can also be used to concatenate data frames along the **column axis (axis = 1).**

```
df3 = pd.DataFrame({'Column4': ['C0', 'C1', 'C2'],
                    'Column3': ['D0', 'D1', 'D2']},
                index=[0, 1, 2])


# Concatenating the data frames along the column axis
result = pd.concat([df1, df3], axis=1)
result
```

The resulting concatenated data frame is created based on **appending the columns side by side**. The parameter of **axis = 1** is used to do the same.

	Column1	Column2	Column3	Column4	Column3
0	A0	B0	D0	C0	D0
1	A1	B1	D1	C1	D1
2	A2	B2	D2	C2	D2

Figure 3.21: Concatenated data frame along the column

Merge

The `merge` operation in pandas combines data frames into one data frame by joining rows using one or more keys. It is similar to the JOIN operation in SQL.

The following code explains the merge function.

```
# Creating the first DataFrame
df1 = pd.DataFrame({
    'Employee': ['Tom', 'Ben', 'Tom','Suzy'],
    'Department': ['IT', 'Marketing', 'IT', 'R&D']
})


# Creating the second DataFrame
df2 = pd.DataFrame({
    'Employee': ['Tom', 'Suzy'],
    'Salary': [8000, 10000]
```

```
})
```

```
merged_df = pd.merge(df1, df2, on='Employee')
merged_df
```

This code has **2 data frames df1 and df2** with the **Employee name and Department** in **df1** and the **Employee name and Salary** in **df2**. The merge operation is used to combine both the data frames on the **Employee column** as we use in JOIN in SQL.

The resulting data frame is as follows:

	Employee	Department	Salary
0	Tom	IT	8000
1	Tom	IT	8000
2	Suzy	R&D	10000

Figure 3.22: Merged data frames df1 and df2 on the Employee column

The next merge operation is the **left join operation of SQL**. Here, we are merging df1 and df2 as before but only considering **all the rows of df1** and the **common rows between df1 and df2**.

```
merged_df = pd.merge(df1, df2, on='Employee', how='left')
merged_df
```

The preceding code is the same as before with an addition of the **how='left'** parameter which considers **all the rows of the left data frame (df1)**. If we use how='**right**', then **all the rows of the right data frame (df2)** will be considered.

	Employee	Department	Salary
0	Tom	IT	8000.0
1	Ben	Marketing	NaN
2	Tom	IT	8000.0
3	Suzy	R&D	10000.0

Figure 3.23: Left joining of the data frames using the merge function

Join

The `.join()` function is used to combine data frames based on their indices. It is very similar to the `.merge()` function mentioned earlier but it uses the **indices to join the data frames** unlike **columns in the** `.merge()` function. It does the left join like above and if there is **no match in certain rows, the result is NaN**.

```
left = pd.DataFrame({'A': ['A0', 'A1', 'A2']}, index=['x', 'y', 'z'])
right = pd.DataFrame({'B': ['B0', 'B1', 'B2']}, index=['x', 'a', 'b'])
joined = left.join(right)
joined
```

The preceding code uses the `.join()` function and the data frames **df1** and **df2** are joined based on the indices.

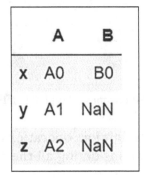

Figure 3.24: *Resulting data frame after the Join function is used*

Bonus Libraries for Data Cleaning

The data cleaning and preparation process is done by traditional Python libraries like **pandas, numpy, scipy**, and so on, but there are other libraries too, like `pyjanitor`, `ftfy`, and `polars` which are very good alternatives to the former libraries. So, let's discuss some of them briefly.

Pyjanitor

`Pyjanitor` is an open-source Python library built on top of the **Janitor package in R programming**. It does the cleaning process with the help of the chaining method, where it removes, renames, deletes columns, removes missing values, and so on. It is very similar to **the pipe operator used in R programming**. The following link brilliantly demonstrates the usage of the Pyjanitor package.

https://www.analyticsvidhya.com/blog/2022/04/a-complete-guide-to-pyjanitor-for-data-cleaning/

Ftfy

The `ftfy` library is called **fixes text for you** and it helps to fix issues related to Unicode encoding and decoding. It is very common in .xlsx or .csv files where some texts are converted to irrelevant texts. Here, if the `ftfy` library is used on those texts, can give us clean text and we can analyze it. The following link shows the usage of the library.

https://pypi.org/project/ftfy/

Polars

Polars is the **pandas** alternative library used to process data faster than the conventional **pandas** library. Polars does not use an index for the data frame in comparison to pandas, it supports more parallel operations than pandas, moreover, **Polars** supports **lazy evaluation** which helps efficient memory usage by examining the queries and optimizing them. In comparison, pandas use the **eager evaluation** technique which evaluates a query without examining or optimizing it thus increasing memory usage. A more detailed explanation of the **comparison of polars and pandas** is explained in the following link:

https://towardsdatascience.com/pandas-vs-polars-a-syntax-and-speed-comparison-5aa54e27497e

Ensuring Data Consistency and Comparability

A **uniform and accurate data** across several access points or instances can be considered as consistent data. This can entail dealing with **format changes, duplicate data, and missing data**. Consistent information encourages **accuracy and usability** and may be essential for making wise decisions.

The goal of data comparability, on the other hand, is to make sure that data gathered using **various methods or sources may be usefully compared**. This frequently entails standardizing **data formats, sizes, and units,** as well as correcting any differences that might develop as a **result of various metadata or data collection techniques**.

Data Consistency

Data consistency assures that there is no conflicting or contradictory information and that the data is accurate and reliable. Consistency checks compare data from different datasets or from the same dataset to find discrepancies and fix them. This may entail cross-validating data, confirming the connections between variables, and spotting any discrepancies in the data.

Data consistency checks can be carried out using methods such as **data profiling, data visualization, and statistical analysis. Data profiling** offers a **deeper knowledge of the data's properties by providing summary statistics and descriptive information** about the data. Techniques for **data visualization**, such as **scatter plots and box plots**, can be used to **locate potential discrepancies or outliers**. The **correlations and consistency** of the data can be further validated **using statistical analysis techniques like correlation analysis or hypothesis testing**.

Data Comparability

The ability to **compare and analyze data from various sources or eras is known as data comparability. Aligning data formats, addressing discrepancies in data definitions or units, and harmonizing** variables across datasets are all necessary to achieve data comparability.

Standardization and Normalization are essential for attaining data comparability. Datasets can be combined and compared with ease if **similar formatting, naming rules, and data types are used**. Additionally, resolving measurement inconsistencies or accounting for inflation can assist in ensuring that data is similar across time.

Conclusion

In this chapter, we explored the process of cleaning and preparing data for analysis. Data cleaning and preparation are crucial steps in the data analysis workflow, as they ensure that the data is accurate, consistent, and suitable for analysis. We discussed various techniques and concepts related to **data cleaning and preparation, including identifying and fixing errors, transforming data, data normalization, data integration, and ensuring data consistency and comparability**.

Data cleaning involves identifying and addressing errors, inconsistencies, and missing values in the dataset. We discussed techniques such as **handling missing**

data, handling outliers, and dealing with inconsistent values. By applying these techniques, we can improve the quality of the data and reduce the risk of biased or incorrect analysis results.

Data preparation involves transforming the data into a suitable format for analysis. We discussed techniques such as **data formatting and standardization, data integration and merging, and data transformation and feature engineering**. These techniques help in harmonizing the data, resolving differences between datasets, and creating new variables based on domain knowledge or insights from the data.

Data normalization is an important step in data preparation, especially when dealing with variables that have different scales or units of measurement. We discussed normalization techniques such as **min-max scaling and z-score scaling**, which bring the variables to a common scale and facilitate fair comparisons.

Ensuring data consistency and comparability is crucial when working with multiple datasets or data collected at different time points. We discussed techniques such as **standardization, data profiling, and statistical analysis** to ensure that the data is consistent, comparable, and reliable across different sources or periods.

Throughout the chapter, we provided code examples and discussed the use of popular libraries such as **NumPy, Pandas, Scipy**, for data cleaning and preparation tasks, and also explained the libraries of `polars`, `Pyjanitor`, and `Ftfy` in brief. These libraries offer powerful functions and methods to handle various aspects of data cleaning and preparation efficiently.

By investing time and effort in **cleaning and preparing the data, we can ensure that the subsequent analysis is based on accurate, consistent, and reliable data**. This improves the quality and integrity of the analysis results and enables informed decision-making based on trustworthy insights.

In the next chapter, we will delve into exploratory data analysis techniques, which help us gain a deeper understanding of the data, identify patterns, and uncover meaningful insights.

## CHAPTER 4

Exploratory Data Analysis

Introduction

Exploratory Data Analysis (EDA) is the most important step in the data analysis process. It involves investigating and understanding the patterns, and relationships within a dataset before conducting further deeper analysis or building predictive models. EDA aids analysts in gaining insights, spotting problems with data quality, and selecting the best data preparation options. This chapter will **explain EDA and its importance**, the **process of EDA as carried out during the data science lifecycle**, various data analysis exploration methods like **descriptive statistics, data distribution analysis, correlation analysis, dimensionality reduction, some visualization techniques, time series analysis, some auto EDA tools like pandas profiling and d-tale, and some real-life use cases**. However, the topics of visualization and time series will also be discussed in detail dedicatedly in separate chapters.

Structure

In this chapter, we will discuss the following topics:

- Introduction to Exploratory Data Analysis (EDA)
  - Importance of EDA
  - The whole EDA Process
- Data Analysis Methods for Exploration
  - Descriptive Statistics
  - Data Distribution Analysis

- o Correlation Analysis
- o Dimensionality Reduction
- Visualizations for Exploring Data
  - o Univariate Visualizations
  - o Bivariate Visualizations
  - o Multivariate Visualizations
- Identifying Patterns and Trends
  - o Cluster Analysis
- Auto EDA Tools (pandas profiling and d-tale)
- Case Studies

Introduction to Exploratory Data Analysis (EDA)

Exploratory Data Analysis is an approach that summarizes the **important properties of the data, uncovering the underlying patterns, and identifying the outliers or anomalies.** It involves **visualizing data using graphs, charts, and statistical measures** to reveal meaningful information.

Importance of EDA

EDA understands the data by identifying the flaws and making informed and intelligent decisions in the whole data analysis process. It identifies missing values, outliers, and other anomalies, and does feature selection and engineering to create a solid foundation for advanced statistical analysis.

The whole EDA Process

The EDA process typically involves the following steps:

- **Data collection:** Gather the relevant dataset from various sources like web scraping, databases, accessing APIs, surveys, and so on.
- **Data cleaning:** Preprocess the data by handling missing values, outliers, anomalies, removing duplicates, and so on.
- **Data exploration:** Uses descriptive statistics, visualizations, correlation analysis, and other analytical techniques to gain relevant insights from the data.

- **Hypothesis generation:** Formulate hypotheses based on the initial findings and patterns observed.
- **Summary and insights:** Summarize the key findings and insights derived from the EDA process.

Data Analysis Methods for Exploration

The Data Analysis methods for exploration are **descriptive statistics, data distribution analysis, correlation analysis, and dimensionality reduction**. The individual topics are explained along with the code.

Descriptive Statistics

Descriptive Statistics is the fundamental block of data analysis and machine learning modeling. It helps in summarizing the data using the relevant Python libraries. It can be applied to various datasets and variables using the **Pandas library in Python**. The central tendency (mean, median, mode) and the variations in the data (variance and standard deviation) are being calculated.

To demonstrate the concept of descriptive statistics, we use the **QS World University Rankings 2024** retrieved from **https://www.kaggle.com/datasets/joebeachcapital/qs-world-university-rankings-2024**

```
import pandas as pd
df= pd.read_csv('2024 QS World University Rankings 1.1 (For qs.com).csv')
df.head()
```

	2024 RANK	2023 RANK	Institution Name	Country Code	Country	SIZE	FOCUS	RES.	AGE	STATUS	...	International Faculty Rank	International Students Score	International Students Rank	Internati Rese Netw s
0	rank display	rank display2	institution	location code	location	size	focus	research	age band	status	...	ifr rank	isr score	isr rank	irn s
1	1	1	Massachusetts Institute of Technology (MIT)	US	United States	M	CO	VH	5	B	...	56	88.2	128	
2	2	2	University of Cambridge	UK	United Kingdom	L	FC	VH	5	A	...	64	95.8	85	
3	3	4	University of Oxford	UK	United Kingdom	L	FC	VH	5	A	...	110	98.2	60	
4	4	5	Harvard University	US	United States	L	FC	VH	5	B	...	210	66.8	223	

5 rows × 29 columns

Figure 4.1: *The first 5 rows of the data frame*

```
df = df.drop(index=0)
df.info()
```

The first row is deleted because it is repeated.

```
<class 'pandas.core.frame.DataFrame'>
RangeIndex: 1497 entries, 1 to 1497
Data columns (total 29 columns):
 #   Column                                Non-Null Count  Dtype
---  ------                                --------------  -----
 0   2024 RANK                             1497 non-null   object
 1   2023 RANK                             1415 non-null   object
 2   Institution Name                      1497 non-null   object
 3   Country Code                          1497 non-null   object
 4   Country                               1497 non-null   object
 5   SIZE                                  1474 non-null   object
 6   FOCUS                                 1496 non-null   object
 7   RES.                                  1410 non-null   object
 8   AGE                                   1471 non-null   object
 9   STATUS                                1455 non-null   object
 10  Academic Reputation Score             1497 non-null   object
 11  Academic Reputation Rank              1497 non-null   object
 12  Employer Reputation Score             1496 non-null   object
 13  Employer Reputation Rank              1496 non-null   object
 14  Faculty Student Score                 1473 non-null   object
 15  Faculty Student Rank                  1473 non-null   object
 16  Citations per Faculty Score           1473 non-null   object
 17  Citations per Faculty Rank            1473 non-null   object
 18  International Faculty Score            1371 non-null   object
 19  International Faculty Rank            1371 non-null   object
 20  International Students Score           1417 non-null   object
 21  International Students Rank            1417 non-null   object
 22  International Research Network Score   1493 non-null   object
 23  International Research Network Rank    1493 non-null   object
 24  Employment Outcomes Score             1473 non-null   object
 25  Employment Outcomes Rank              1473 non-null   object
 26  Sustainability Score                  1397 non-null   object
 27  Sustainability Rank                   1397 non-null   object
 28  Overall SCORE                         1497 non-null   object
dtypes: object(29)
memory usage: 339.3+ KB
```

Figure 4.2: *The datatypes of all the attributes and the total number of rows*

The preceding screenshot is the output of `df.info()` and it shows the details of all the variables, **their datatypes** (most of them are object datatypes and we will change them to float or integer as per the need), the **number of entries that have values** (and also gives us an idea about the number of missing values). It also shows that there are **29 columns in the data frame**.

There are several columns with numerical values but all of them are **represented as object datatype**, so we need to **change it to float datatype.** The object datatype means the variable is alphanumeric. For the machine learning model or for any analysis purpose we need **numerical data in integer/float format and categorial data in categorical format** which **can be later converted into**

numerical form using one hot encoding. By converting the variables into their respective datatype, the data analysis and ML model training become easy.

```
df['Sustainability Score '] = df['Sustainability Score'].astype(float)
```

The **.describe()** method is used to get the descriptive statistics of the column in the data frame.

```
df['Sustainability Score '].describe()
```

The result of the descriptive statistics is as follows.

```
count    1397.000000
mean       25.429349
std        31.014888
min         1.000000
25%         1.400000
50%         8.400000
75%        42.600000
max       100.000000
Name: Sustainability Score , dtype: float64
```

Figure 4.3: *The Descriptive Statistics of the Sustainability Score variable are found*

The **maximum score is 100,** but the **median lies at 8.4. The mean is 25.42** and the **minimum value is 1.** The **top 25% (75th percentile)** of the data is having **a score of more than 42.6.** This denotes that the majority of the scores lie below 42 and only a **few universities have good sustainability scores**.

Moreover, the descriptive statistics can also be calculated using the following codes:

```
df['Sustainability Score '].mean()
df['Sustainability Score '].median()
df['Sustainability Score '].std()
df['Sustainability Score '].mode()
```

The **.mode()** object normally is used to **find the frequency of the categories,** that is, they are **used for categorical variables** instead of numerical variables.

Data Distribution Analysis

Data Distribution analysis in Python is the observing of the distribution and relationships within the data. Normally, the **Pandas, Numpy, and Seaborn** libraries are used to perform the operation. Distributions like **Histogram, KDE plot (Kernel Density Estimation), ECDF (Empirical Cumulative Distribution Function) plot, Violin plot, QQ Plot (Quantile -Quantile Plot), Box plot, and Rug plot** are used to study the data in detail.

Histogram

Histogram represents numerical variables by their distribution. The `.histplot()` object is used from the **Seaborn library**.

```
import seaborn as sns
sns.histplot(df['Sustainability Score '])
```

The histogram of the Sustainability score is as follows:

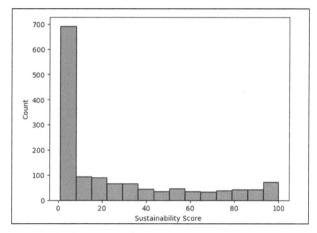

Figure 4.4: *The histogram distribution of the Sustainability Score*

KDE Plot

The **Kernel Density Estimate (KDE)** plot is used to represent the data using a continuous probability distribution curve. The `kdeplot()` function is used to create the plot.

```
sns.kdeplot(df['Sustainability Score '])
```

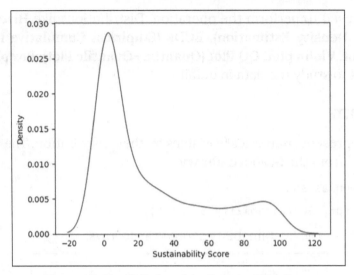

Figure 4.5: *The KDE plot of the Sustainability Score*

ECDF plot

The **Empirical Cumulative Distribution Function (ECDF)** plot represents the proportion or count of observations falling below each unique value in the dataset. The `ecdfplot()` function is used to create the plot. The observations are visualized directly, that is, there are no binning or smoothing parameters.

```
sns.ecdfplot(df['Sustainability Score '])
```

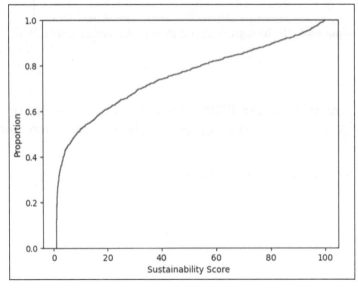

Figure 4.6: *The ECDF plot of the Sustainability Score*

QQ plot

A **Q-Q (quantile-quantile)** plot is a probability plot for comparing two probability distributions by plotting their quantiles against each other.

```
import scipy.stats as stats
import matplotlib.pyplot as plt


stats.probplot(df['Sustainability Score '], dist="norm", plot=plt)
plt.show()
```

The code shows the usage of the **stats library** and the **.probplot()** function **using the normal distribution (dist="norm")**. The plot is shown as follows.

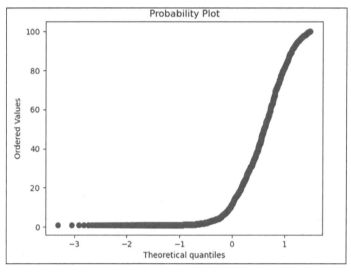

Figure 4.7: *The Q-Q plot of the Sustainability Score*

Correlation Analysis

Correlation analysis is an important component of EDA where it is found out whether any relationship exists between two variables and datasets and, of course, how strong or weak the relationship is. It is imperative to understand the correlation between variables to understand the innate patterns and connections within the dataset. For example, we need to perform the correlation analysis of student performance on tests versus their studying hours, or student performance on tests versus active attendance (that is, the student is asking questions and is involved in curriculum-based conversations) of the class.

The **positive correlation** means that both variables increase with respect to each other, on the contrary, the **negative correlation** signifies that if one variable increases, the other decreases.

https://www.kaggle.com/datasets/vikasukani/diabetes-data-set?select=diabetes-dataset.csv

To proceed forward, let's take an example of the diabetes dataset which was used for testing and explanation here. The code is given as follows.

```
import pandas as pd
# Load the dataset
df = pd.read_csv('diabetes-dataset.csv')
df.head()
```

	Pregnancies	Glucose	BloodPressure	SkinThickness	Insulin	BMI	DiabetesPedigreeFunction	Age	Outcome
0	2	138	62	35	0	33.6	0.127	47	1
1	0	84	82	31	125	38.2	0.233	23	0
2	0	145	0	0	0	44.2	0.630	31	1
3	0	135	68	42	250	42.3	0.365	24	1
4	1	139	62	41	480	40.7	0.536	21	0

Figure 4.8: The first 5 rows of the diabetes dataset and all the variables are numeric

In the dataset, all the variables are numeric be it integer or float, but the Outcome variable is 1 or 0 meaning if it is **1 then the person is likely to have diabetes** and **0 means the person is not likely to have diabetes**. The attributes of **Glucose, Blood Pressure, Skin Thickness, Insulin, BMI**, and so on, affect the probability of a patient suffering from diabetes. This **dataset is ideal for explaining the concept of correlation analysis** since all these attributes and the correlation numbers later can help us understand whether a patient suffers from diabetes or not.

The **datatypes of the dataset are checked** once to identify if there are any mismatched datatypes, for example, numeric but identified as an object.

```
print(df.dtypes)
```

```
Pregnancies                          int64
Glucose                              int64
BloodPressure                        int64
SkinThickness                        int64
Insulin                              int64
BMI                                  float64
DiabetesPedigreeFunction             float64
Age                                  int64
Outcome                              int64
dtype: object
```

Figure 4.9: *The datatypes of the dataset are identified as numeric*

There is the `corr()` method in **Pandas** to calculate the **pairwise correlation of the columns, excluding the NA/null** values. The method returns a **correlation matrix which is a table** showing correlation coefficients between the variables. Each cell in the table shows the correlation between the variables.

```
# Compute the correlation matrix
corr_matrix = df.corr()
```

The correlation matrix for all the variables is shown in the figure as follows.

	Pregnancies	Glucose	BloodPressure	SkinThickness	Insulin	BMI	DiabetesPedigreeFunction	Age	Outcome
Pregnancies	1.000000	0.120405	0.149672	-0.063375	-0.076600	0.019475	-0.025453	0.539457	0.224437
Glucose	0.120405	1.000000	0.138044	0.062368	0.320371	0.226864	0.123243	0.254496	0.458421
BloodPressure	0.149672	0.138044	1.000000	0.198800	0.087384	0.281545	0.051331	0.238375	0.075958
SkinThickness	-0.063375	0.062368	0.198800	1.000000	0.448859	0.393760	0.178299	-0.111034	0.076040
Insulin	-0.076600	0.320371	0.087384	0.448859	1.000000	0.223012	0.192719	-0.085879	0.120924
BMI	0.019475	0.226864	0.281545	0.393760	0.223012	1.000000	0.125719	0.038987	0.276726
DiabetesPedigreeFunction	-0.025453	0.123243	0.051331	0.178299	0.192719	0.125719	1.000000	0.026569	0.155459
Age	0.539457	0.254496	0.238375	-0.111034	-0.085879	0.038987	0.026569	1.000000	0.236509
Outcome	0.224437	0.458421	0.075958	0.076040	0.120924	0.276726	0.155459	0.236509	1.000000

Figure 4.10: *The pairwise correlation of the columns*

The **correlation values** are between **-1** and **1**, and the **number which is near 1 is a positively correlated number** meaning that the 2 variables are increasing (or decreasing) together, and if the **number is closer to -1**, then the **2 variables are inversely correlated to each other** (if one increases, the other decreases). If the number is 0, **then there isn't any positive or negative correlation** between the variables or there is no relationship.

If we observe the numbers cell by cell, **higher glucose level** contributes to a **higher probability of diabetes-affected patients** and the correlation number is

0.4584. **Higher Insulin level is directly proportional to higher skin thickness** (correlation coefficient is 0.4488). As Age increases, skin thickness decreases (correlation coefficient -0.111).

Spearman Correlation

Spearman correlation does not assume a linear relationship or normal distribution, and it's based on the ranked values for each variable rather than the raw data. It is mostly used to calculate the correlation coefficients for ordinal variables.

```
# Compute the Spearman correlation matrix
spearman_corr_matrix = df.corr(method='spearman')
print("\nSpearman Correlation Matrix: ")
spearman_corr_matrix
```

The correlation matrix is as follows.

Spearman Correlation Matrix:

	Pregnancies	Glucose	BloodPressure	SkinThickness	Insulin	BMI	DiabetesPedigreeFunction	Age	Outcome
Pregnancies	1.000000	0.113963	0.177586	-0.072205	-0.133894	-0.006969	-0.039908	0.598020	0.195180
Glucose	0.113963	1.000000	0.218068	0.072516	0.222479	0.227460	0.071894	0.269762	0.471294
BloodPressure	0.177586	0.218068	1.000000	0.147944	-0.007185	0.286740	0.028455	0.350188	0.154092
SkinThickness	-0.072205	0.072516	0.147944	1.000000	0.533525	0.468604	0.175107	-0.053869	0.094745
Insulin	-0.133894	0.222479	-0.007185	0.533525	1.000000	0.218913	0.232121	-0.123015	0.062963
BMI	-0.006969	0.227460	0.286740	0.468604	0.218913	1.000000	0.138046	0.122502	0.299805
DiabetesPedigreeFunction	-0.039908	0.071894	0.028455	0.175107	0.232121	0.138046	1.000000	0.036910	0.148650
Age	0.598020	0.269762	0.350188	-0.053869	-0.123015	0.122502	0.036910	1.000000	0.310411
Outcome	0.195180	0.471294	0.154092	0.094745	0.062963	0.299805	0.148650	0.310411	1.000000

Figure 4.11: *The Spearman correlation of the columns*

Let's check out the correlation matrix using Seaborn's heatmap function.

```
import seaborn as sns
f, ax = plt.subplots(figsize = (12,10))
sns.heatmap(df.corr(),
            annot = True,
            linecolor = 'r',
            linewidths = .5,
            fmt = '.1f',
            ax = ax);
```

The **correlation matrix** is represented in the form of a heatmap as shown in the following figure. The numbers are the same as the `df.corr()` function we used earlier.

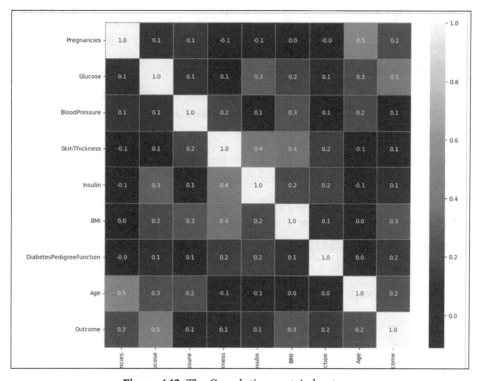

Figure 4.12: *The Correlation matrix heatmap*

The **correlation coefficient of 0.5** between **glucose** and the **outcome** suggests that both variables are **positively correlated**.

Dimensionality Reduction

Dimensionality reduction is the process of reducing the number of random variables by obtaining a set of principal variables. Sometimes the dataset has a high number of features and we need to reduce the features so that **irrelevant features are removed and most of the information from the features is retained for the further process**.

It is divided into feature selection and feature extraction.

Principal Component Analysis (PCA) is a common dimensionality reduction technique. It is a statistical technique of **orthogonally transforming the n dimensions of a dataset into a new set of n dimensions**. It analyzes the data where the observations are described by a lot of inter-correlated quantitative dependent variables. It extracts important information from the data and displays the information as a set of orthogonal variables.

Let's do some code to understand the workings of the PCA technique.

```
from sklearn.preprocessing import StandardScaler
from sklearn.decomposition import PCA
```

The **sklearn library** is used which has the **StandardScaler function** for standardizing the features and the **PCA function** for performing the PCA operation.

Since the data frame is already present from the previous correlation analysis, we next proceed to separate the **target variable (Outcome)** from the **mother data frame (df).**

```
# Separate the features from the target column ('Outcome')
X = df.drop('Outcome', axis=1)
y = df['Outcome']
```

This way we have a separate variable y which is the output attribute.

Next, we proceed to standardize the features since PCA is influenced by the scales of the features. We standardize the features to have a **mean of 0 and a standard deviation of 1.**

```
# Standardize the features
scaler = StandardScaler()
X = scaler.fit_transform(X)
```

Next, the PCA technique is applied to the X variable to **reduce the dimensionality of the data to 2 principal components.**

```
# Apply PCA
pca = PCA(n_components=2) # we are reducing to 2 principal components
X_pca = pca.fit_transform(X)


# Print the explained variance ratio
print('Explained variance ratio: ', pca.explained_variance_ratio_)


Explained variance ratio: [0.26153728 0.21691186]
```

The explained variance ratio tells how much **variance can be attributed to each of the principal components** (dimensions). Since the **dimensions were reduced from 4 to 2**, some of the variance is lost too.

Finally, visualize the data.

```
# Visualize the results
plt.scatter(X_pca[:, 0], X_pca[:, 1], c=y)
plt.xlabel('First Principal Component')
plt.ylabel('Second Principal Component')
plt.show()
```

The scatter plot of the 2 components is as follows.

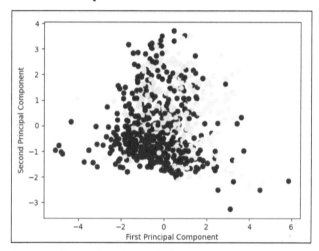

Figure 4.13: *Visualizing the PCA with dimension reduced to 2 components*

The code uses the scatter plot to represent the 2 dimensions. **X_pca is used along with 2 dimensions and the output variable y**. The data points are segregated by 2 colors and are mostly congested in the middle of the plot.

Visualizations for Exploring Data

Exploratory Data Analysis (EDA) has a lot of steps involved starting from **data preparation to descriptive statistics to correlation analysis to cluster analysis to visualizations** and so on. Visualizations make up a significant portion of EDA where **graphs, plots, charts,** and so on, are used to **tell stories to the audience**. They not **only look visually pleasing but also explain the numbers with the help of charts, plots, and graphs**. They help the **analysts, and the managers make informed decisions based on visual representations**. For example, the sales of any video game can be understood by factors that are represented in a pie chart. By looking at the pie chart itself, the managers can make informed decisions on how to improve the sales for the next quarter.

Univariate Analysis

Univariate analysis is the simplest form of data analysis, where the data being analyzed contains only one variable. Since it's just one variable, **it doesn't have to do anything with causes or relationships**. The main purpose of univariate analysis is to describe the data and find patterns that exist within it. Let's create a histogram for the Glucose variable in the diabetes dataset we have been using.

```
# Plot histogram for the 'Glucose' column
plt.hist(df['Glucose'], bins=10, alpha=0.5)
plt.title('Histogram for Glucose')
plt.xlabel('Glucose')
plt.ylabel('Frequency')
plt.show()
```

The histogram representation is shown as follows.

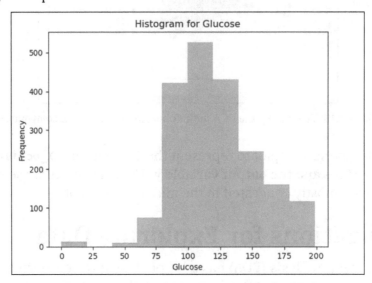

Figure 4.14: *Univariate analysis using Histogram*

The preceding histogram shows that most of the Glucose levels are between **80** and **150 units approximately.** The graph is a left-skewed one where most of the data is concentrated toward the right.

Bivariate Analysis

Bivariate analysis, as the name suggests, involves 2 variables and we find the relationship between them. Here is a scatter plot (a common bivariate plot) for the **Glucose** and **Insulin** variables from the diabetes dataset.

```
#Bivariate Analysis
# Scatter plot for 'Glucose' and 'Insulin'
sns.scatterplot(x='Glucose', y='Insulin', data=df)
plt.title('Scatter plot of Glucose and Insulin')
plt.show()
```

The scatter plot function we have used here is straightforward and has tested using the 2 variables of Insulin and Glucose. Now let's check how the plot looks like a visualization graph.

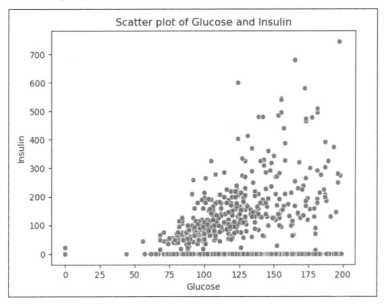

Figure 4.15: *Bivariate analysis using Scatter Plot*

The preceding scatter plot shows a very **close linear relationship but not a straightforward linear one**. Most of the data is concentrated between **80 and 150 glucose units as we observed from the univariate analysis. Insulin intake increases with increasing glucose levels** but there are also certain outliers in the beginning where 0 glucose and 0 insulin levels are there. There are also a **couple of outliers at the top right**.

Multivariate Analysis

In multivariate analysis, we focus **on multiple variables** and try to understand the relationship between them. In this case, we will test with 4 variables namely, **Pregnancies, Glucose, Blood Pressure, and Insulin** closely related to the target **Outcome** variable and understand the relationship between them. We have used the `pairplot()` function to perform the operation.

```
#Multivariate Analysis
# Pair plot for 'Pregnancies', 'Glucose', 'BloodPressure', 'Insulin'
sns.pairplot(df[['Pregnancies', 'Glucose', 'BloodPressure', 'Insulin']])
plt.show()
```

The seaborn library has the `pairplot()` function that can be used to perform multivariate analysis. The pairplot is shown as follows.

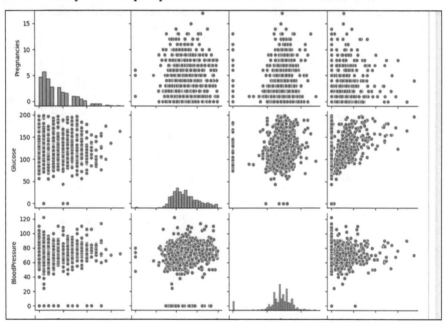

Figure 4.16: *Multivariate analysis using Pair Plot*

The preceding **pairplot** shows the relationship between the 4 variables. There are 16 plots but due to lack of space, all of them could not be shown in the preceding screenshot. One can easily test it out in their system for a better understanding.

All the subplots are not relevant, for example, the **Glucose versus pregnancies plot does not give us any information** since the scatter subplot does not follow any specific positive or negative relationship, the same goes for **Pregnancies versus**

Blood Pressure, **Blood Pressure versus Insulin**, and a few more. **Glucose and Insulin** show a **positive relationship (a very close to a linear relationship)**. This way, we can study and observe relations between multiple variables simultaneously.

Identifying Patterns and Trends

For identifying patterns and trends in the dataset, there must be some kind of technique to go through the process of understanding the patterns. For example, in the **unsupervised machine learning** technique, there is **no target specified** beforehand, thus the algorithm needs to understand and segregate similar kinds of data points in groups like clustering.

Cluster Analysis

As previously stated, Cluster Analysis is a technique for **categorizing a dataset into groups or clusters in which comparable data points are placed in one group** and dissimilar data points are placed in other groups. K-means clustering is one of the most widely used clustering methods. The K-means technique separates a **set of n datasets into k subsets (or clusters)**, with each dataset assigned to the **cluster with the closest mean or centroid.**

Let's apply the K-means clustering on the diabetes dataset using the **sklearn library.**

```
from sklearn.cluster import KMeans


# Separate the features from the target column ('Outcome')
X = df.drop('Outcome', axis=1)


# Apply K-means clustering
kmeans = KMeans(n_clusters=2, random_state=0)  # we are choosing 2 clus-
ters
kmeans.fit(X)


# Print the cluster centers
print('Cluster centers: ', kmeans.cluster_centers_)
```

```
Cluster centers:  [[ 0.97680787   0.39379477   0.38518391 -0.21659583
-0.16202733   0.08989272

   0.00323192   1.05962701]
 [-0.51678214 -0.20833791 -0.20378231   0.11459045   0.08572088
-0.04755792

  -0.00170985 -0.56059778]]
```

Since we are still using the diabetes dataset, we need to focus on **importing the KMeans function** from the **sklearn library**. We separate the **features (X) and the target column (y)**. Then we apply K-means clustering to the features. The **n_clusters** parameter is the **number of clusters** to form and the number of centroids to generate. The **random_state** parameter is used for the reproducibility of the results. Next, we print the cluster centers. Next, we need to visualize the clusters.

```
# Visualize the clusters

plt.scatter(X[:,1], X[:,4], c=kmeans.labels_, cmap='viridis')


# Plot the cluster centers

plt.scatter(kmeans.cluster_centers_[:, 0], kmeans.cluster_centers_[:,
1], s=300, c='red')

plt.title('Clusters of Patients')

plt.xlabel('Glucose')

plt.ylabel('Insulin')

plt.show()
```

In the first line of code for visualization, we keep all the data points in **2 clusters of different colors** (yellow and purple). The data points are not completely segregated but can be understood overall. The Glucose and Insulin variables are considered in this case. That's why its **X[:,1] and X[:,4]**. There are 2000 **kmeans. labels_** for the clustering.

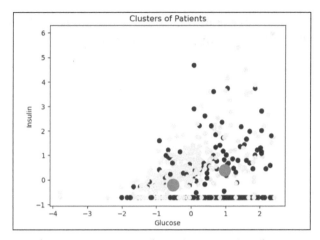

Figure 4.17: *K-Means clustering operation shown*

In the next part, the clustering operation **2 groups are formed** as shown by the **2 big red dots**. Most of the yellow points are there with the left red dot and the other points are with the purple dot (as shown in *Figure 4.17*).

Auto EDA tools (pandas profiling and D-tale)

Till now we have been primarily dealing with Exploratory Data Analysis and their steps like **Descriptive Statistics, Correlation Analysis, Cluster Analysis, Visualizations, Data Distribution Analysis, Feature Engineering techniques**, and so on. All these techniques can be implemented altogether using libraries **dtale** and **pandas-profiling** (https://pypi.org/project/dtale/, https://pypi.org/project/pandas-profiling/). Let's discuss these libraries in detail.

D-tale

D-tale is the **Auto EDA library** that was launched in February 2020 and is used to visualize Pandas data frames conveniently and also supports **various interactive plots, 3D plots, heat maps, the correlation between the features, building custom columns**, and many more. All these operations are normally carried out by different functions but all D-tale does all this together **in detail**. The code is demonstrated as follows.

```
import dtale
d = dtale.show(df)
d.open_browser()
```

We just have to install the **dtale** library and we can do the operation and get the relevant result as shown in the following screenshot.

	Pregnancies	Glucose	BloodPressure	SkinThickness	Insulin	BMI	DiabetesPedigreeFunction	Age	Outcome
0	2	138	62	35	0	33.60	0.13	47	1
1	0	84	82	31	125	38.20	0.23	23	0
2	0	145	0	0	0	44.20	0.63	31	1
3	0	135	68	42	250	42.30	0.37	24	1
4	1	139	62	41	480	40.70	0.54	21	0
5	0	173	78	32	265	46.50	1.16	58	0
6	4	99	72	17	0	25.60	0.29	28	0
7	8	194	80	0	0	26.10	0.55	67	0
8	2	83	65	28	66	36.80	0.63	24	0
9	2	89	90	30	0	33.50	0.29	42	0
10	4	99	68	38	0	32.80	0.15	33	0
11	4	125	70	18	122	28.90	1.14	45	1
12	3	80	0	0	0	0.00	0.17	22	0
13	6	166	74	0	0	26.60	0.30	66	0
14	5	110	68	0	0	26.00	0.29	30	0
15	2	81	72	15	76	30.10	0.55	25	0
16	7	195	70	33	145	25.10	0.16	55	1
17	6	154	74	32	193	29.30	0.84	39	0
18	2	117	90	19	71	25.20	0.31	21	0
19	3	84	72	32	0	37.20	0.27	28	0
20	6	0	68	41	0	39.00	0.73	41	1
21	7	94	64	25	79	33.30	0.74	41	0

Figure 4.18: *D-tale web page representation*

The preceding figure shows how a data frame looks after the D-tale library is used. It looks very descriptive and clear. The **features can be seen** and at the **top left**, the **number of rows (2000)** and the **number of columns (9)** can be observed.

	Pregnancies	Glucose	BloodPressure	SkinThickness	Insulin	BMI	DiabetesPedigreeFunction	Age	Outcome
D-TALE		138	62	35	0	33.60	0.13	47	1
Convert To XArray		84	82	31	125	38.20	0.23	23	0
Describe		145	0	0	0	44.20	0.63	31	1
Custom Filter		135	68	42	250	42.30	0.37	24	1
Show/Hide Columns		139	62	41	480	40.70	0.54	21	0
Dataframe Functions		173	78	32	265	46.50	1.16	58	0
Clean Column		99	72	17	0	25.60	0.29	28	0
Merge & Stack		194	80	0	0	26.10	0.55	67	0
Summarize Data		83	65	28	66	36.80	0.63	24	0
Time Series Analysis		89	90	30	0	33.50	0.29	42	0
Duplicates		99	68	38	0	32.80	0.15	33	0
Missing Analysis		125	70	18	122	28.90	1.14	45	1
Feature Analysis		80	0	0	0	0.00	0.17	22	0
Correlations		166	74	0	0	26.60	0.30	66	0
Predictive Power Score		110	68	0	0	26.00	0.29	30	0
Charts		81	72	15	76	30.10	0.55	25	0
Network Viewer		195	70	33	145	25.10	0.16	55	1
Heat Map [By Col] [Overall]		154	74	32	193	29.30	0.84	39	0
		117	90	19	71	25.20	0.31	21	0
Highlight Dtypes		84	72	32	0	37.20	0.27	28	0
		0	68	41	0	39.00	0.73	41	1
Highlight Missing		94	64	25	79	33.30	0.74	41	0

Figure 4.19: *The play button on the top left gives a list of functionalities*

The functionalities are **custom filter, data frame functions, clean column, merge and stack, Describe, Time Series Analysis, Feature Analysis, Highlight outliers**, and so on. If we drag the slider down, we can find more features.

Now let's explore some features to find how it fares against the conventional EDA techniques.

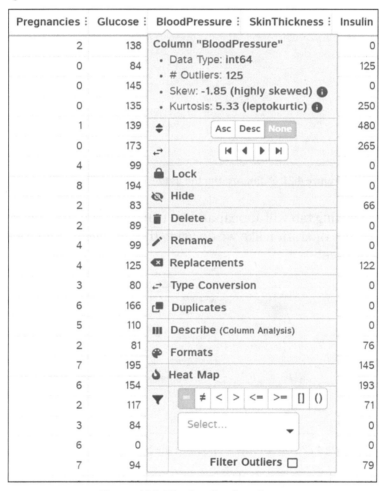

Figure 4.20: *The details of a column*

If we look closely, then we get the **datatype of the variable, the number of outliers, the skew, and kurtosis**. There are also various functions like **delete, replacements, rename, hide, duplicates, and description** of the variable.

We can also summarize the data based on a particular attribute, for example, we are trying to **find the average BMI for each Age**. So, we can use the technique of **Summarizing data** here.

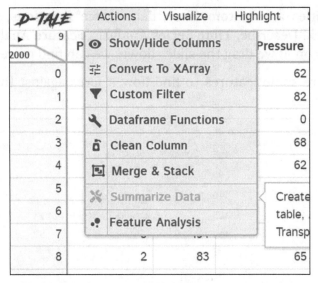

Figure 4.21: *Summarizing the data from the Actions tab*

On this, the following tab will appear and we can then feed the required variables and do the **Groupby** operation like we do using the `.groupby()` **function in Pandas** or **normally in Excel**.

Figure 4.22: *The Groupby option in the Summarize data option*

After this operation is done, we get the result as follows.

D-TALE		Actions		
▶ ⎸ 2		Age ⋮	BMI ⋮	
52				
0		21	28.12	
1		22	29.71	
2		23	31.22	
3		24	33.02	
4		25	31.56	
5		26	36.31	
6		27	32.01	
7		28	34.22	
8		29	33.63	
9		30	29.68	
10		31	34.20	
11		32	34.03	
12		33	31.38	
13		34	30.13	
14		35	34.41	
15		36	33.66	
16		37	31.89	
17		38	35.14	
18		39	31.52	
19		40	36.34	
20		41	35.15	

Figure 4.23: *Average BMI of each Age*

We can also do numerous operations using the **Visualize** tab.

D-TALE	Actions	Visualize	Highlight	Setti
▶ 9	Pregnancies	▦ Describe		Sk
2000				
0	2	⌗ Duplicates		
1	0	⬙ Missing Analysis		
2	0	⁖ Correlations		
3	0	⁖ Predictive Power Score		
4	1	◷ Time Series Analysis		
5	0	⤳ Charts		
6	4	ⵜ Network Viewer		
7	8			
8	2	◉ Gage R & R		
9	2	89	90	

Figure 4.24: *Visualize tab operations*

We can do the operations of **Correlations, Missing Analysis, Predictive Power Score, and Time Series Analysis** which are very handy because all these are available in one library.

We can test with numerous other functions in the D-tale library, so it is left for the readers to test more.

Pandas-profiling

It is a **Python auto EDA** library that generates interactive HTML reports and includes various aspects of the dataset. They are handling **missing values, descriptive statistics of datasets like mean, mode, median, skewness, standard deviation, and so on, and charts like histograms and correlations**.

Let's demonstrate its use by the following code.

```
#importing required packages
import pandas_profiling
import numpy as np


#descriptive statistics
pandas_profiling.ProfileReport(df)
```

The code is straightforward when it comes to explanation. After the last line of the code is run, we get the following screenshot along with a lot of other information for each variable.

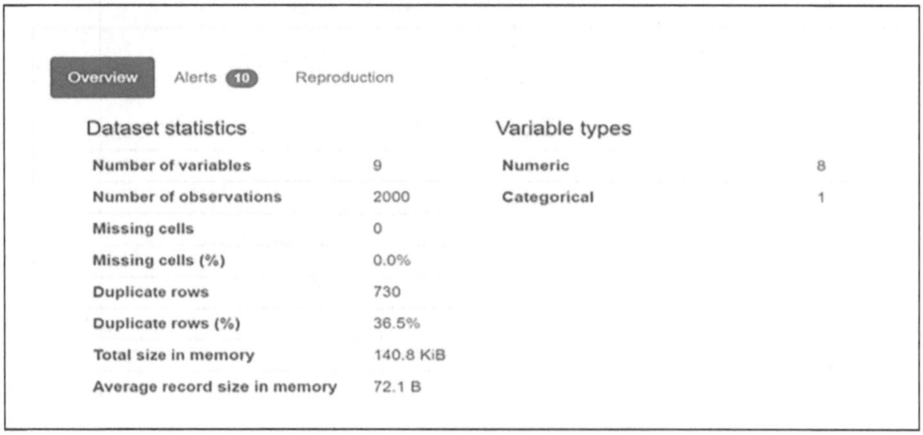

Overview	Alerts 10	Reproduction		
Dataset statistics			**Variable types**	
Number of variables	9		Numeric	8
Number of observations	2000		Categorical	1
Missing cells	0			
Missing cells (%)	0.0%			
Duplicate rows	730			
Duplicate rows (%)	36.5%			
Total size in memory	140.8 KiB			
Average record size in memory	72.1 B			

Figure 4.25: The details of the dataset

In the preceding screenshot, we have the **number of rows, columns, missing values, missing %, duplicate rows, duplicate %**, and so on. It also gives the

number of numeric and categorical variables. If we click on the **Alerts** option, there are certain interesting details.

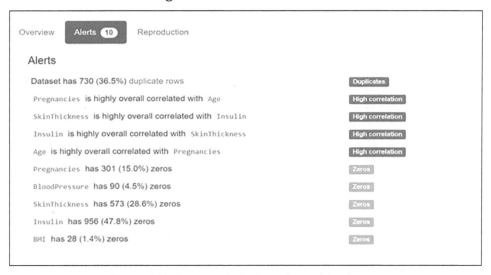

Figure 4.26: *Some statistical numbers of the dataset*

From the preceding screenshot, there are 36.5% duplicate rows, which is a lot. There are interesting results on variables that are highly correlated like **Pregnancies** are highly correlated with **Age**, and **Skin Thickness** is highly correlated with **Insulin level.** Some variables have zeros in them like **Skin Thickness has 28.6% zeros** and **Insulin has 47.8% zeros**.

In the variables section, we can explore more on each attribute like the **Glucose level.**

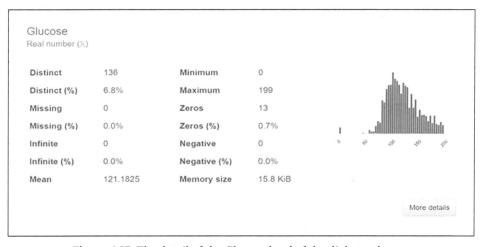

Figure 4.27: *The detail of the Glucose level of the diabetes dataset*

Glucose level variable has **136 distinct values**, the **mean is 121.18**, the **maximum glucose level is 199**, there are **13 zero values in the column**, and **no missing values**.

We also have a heatmap generated by the library which is quite handy.

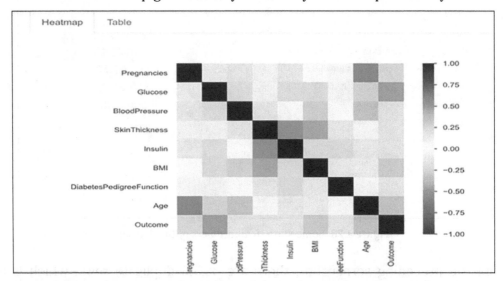

Figure 4.28: *The Heatmap of the dataset showing the correlation between the values*

We also have the details on the **first and last rows, the duplicate rows, the count of missing values**, and so on.

Overall, these **Auto EDA libraries** are a lifesaver when it comes to **performing EDA with many features and saving time**. However, conventional EDA is not going anywhere since it **not only gives a learning curve to the user but also helps us add more features** as we move forward in the data science life cycle. **Conventional EDA** is also not so helpful in dealing with **larger and more complex datasets**.

Case Studies

Exploratory Data Analysis (EDA) can be used to **understand the data, and patterns, identify outliers, and do correlation and cluster analysis**. Here are a few examples to explain the real-life use cases that are normally done at the industry level.

EDA on a Retail Sales Dataset

In the situation of Retail Sales, we have to understand the **sales pattern over the last few years or months, the customer behavior over time, the marketing strategies** used and **their impact on the business, products that are more likely to be bought or that are less likely to be bought**, and so on. Of course, we perform all the EDA techniques we discussed in the chapter, but most importantly the **preceding patterns or trends must come first and they should be the anchor for identifying the business problem and solving it**. For example, we see that there are **certain clothing that are being bought during the festival season by the youth mostly** (but also by the middle-aged and older people), so those specific clothing can be provided with **more discounts and promotions along with certain other accessories like shoes, wallets, belts, caps, and so on. These can be identified by the sales value for each of the items and a correlation analysis can be done**. This way the customer can feel more interested in other items too when needed. Here, the customer will keep coming back to specific items from the store when needed.

EDA on a Healthcare Dataset

For healthcare, it is important to gain insights into patients' health data, and lifestyle choices like how much **exercise he/she does, their level of smoking, and alcohol consumption, overworked or not, stressed or not, normally pleasant mood or not, sugar level, Blood pressure level, height, weight, BMI**, and so on. These factors, if studied well say a lot about a person's physical, mental, and emotional health. The diabetes dataset studied helped us **understand the correlation between the glucose level and the probability of a person having diabetes or not**. There may be other factors too that are responsible for diabetes that were not included in the dataset. If we explore more, for example, there are a **lot of experiments conducted on students who study a lot and don't involve themselves with outdoor activities, talking with their friends, or traveling versus students who do all these along with studying**. The second counterpart has a **lower stress level than the former considering the fact that both of them nearly have the same average grades**. These can also be conducted on professionals of various ages, nationalities, genders, across various kinds of jobs, and so on.

EDA on Finance Dataset

If we explore the financial markets, then we can **identify areas of investment and learn more about money as well as financial management**. These include analyzing stock price data, identifying the trends, and investments done by highly experienced to mid-level experienced investors and learning from them, also understanding how companies perform while the market is doing well, or there is inflation, or exceptional situations like war, pandemic, and so on.

EDA on Manufacturing Dataset

In the manufacturing domain, it is important to understand the factors of production time, production volume, resource usage, and the state of the raw materials. These points can help identify the issues of inefficient utilization of resources and time and thus improve with time. The decision-making can be done accordingly. For example, if there is a chip manufacturing factory that makes **100,000 chips daily, but there are issues with the machinery that limit it to 100,000 but can be increased to 200,000 daily**, then the machinery and the workload can be optimized by the professionals to make certain efficient changes to increase the capacity. This way more demand can be met.

Conclusion

The topic of **Exploratory Data Analysis (EDA)** has been explored quite in detail and the steps covered mostly resonate with what is being practiced in the industry.

The chapter has included various topics from **descriptive statistics to data distribution analysis to correlation analysis to dimensionality reduction to various visualization techniques like univariate, bivariate, and multivariate analysis to cluster analysis and some auto EDA tools like d-tale and pandas-profiling**. These concepts are the backbone of the data science lifecycle and take up most of the time while dealing with datasets and data modeling.

Importance of EDA in the data analysis process

The EDA makes up most of **the time and energy in the data science lifecycle** since we have to **deep dive and understand the data to extract insights, identify data quality issues like missing data, mismatched datatypes, identify outliers in the data columns, missing important columns in some cases**, and so on. All these contribute to the **final goal of data preparation or making intelligent business decisions** for the company. All these factors make the EDA the backbone of the whole data science lifecycle.

Future directions in exploratory data analysis

This chapter concludes with a discussion of EDA, visualizations, exploring various statistical techniques, data cleaning, and various auto EDA and visualization tools that are making a lot of difference in the market. Recently, there has been a rising trend of various AI Chatbot tools too like **ChatGPT, Bard, Perplexity, Bing AI, Phind, Claude, Llama**, and so on, that are doing a fine job of heavy lifting operations like **EDA, data cleaning and preparation, data modeling, machine learning techniques, machine learning operations**, and what not. However, we must never forget it all depends on the developers on what kind of product they are bringing or planning to bring into the market so that they can make use of these tools to create the product. So, they must be well aware of what is happening in the backend.

In the next chapter, we will explore the concepts of **Hypothesis testing, some predictive modeling, regression analysis, and testing, and understanding confidence intervals**. We will build on this chapter and go deeper to extract more important insights that the EDA cannot give us.

Keywords

Exploratory Data Analysis, Data Visualization, Correlation Analysis, Histogram, KDE, Violin plot, Heat map, Dimensionality Reduction, PCA, Cluster Analysis, Auto EDA tools, D-tale, Pandas profiling

## CHAPTER 5

Statistical Analysis

Introduction

Statistics is the main foundation of data science, be it **data cleaning, data preparation, or doing exploratory data analysis**, we cannot just think anything ahead without all the techniques mentioned here. For any data scientist or data analyst, it is of utmost **importance to apply statistical techniques** and have a deeper understanding of the data. In this chapter, we will proceed from the portion where we left off in the previous chapter of *Exploratory Data Analysis* *(EDA)*. We will cover the topics of descriptive statistics like **mean, median, mode, variance, and standard deviation** in detail over the previous chapters, and explore distributions like **Normal, Poisson, Lambda, Binomial, Long-tailed, Student t-test, Chi-Squared**, and so on. We will also learn and experiment with statistical experiences and significance testing like **student t-test, hypothesis testing, A/B testing, regression testing, Degrees of Freedom, Fischers test**, and **Analysis of Variance (ANOVA)** to name a few. There are some libraries like `statsmodels`, `scipy`, `PyMC3` apart from conventional packages of **Pandas** and **Numpy**. As usual from the previous chapters, we will not only learn the theoretical concepts but also use them to solve problems like the use cases we did.

Structure

In this chapter, we will discuss the following topics:

- Introduction to Statistical Analysis
  - Importance of Statistical Analysis
- Statistical Analysis Workflow
  - Data Exploration
  - Variable Selection

- o Statistical Tests
- o Interpretation of Results
- o Reporting and Visualization
- Statistical Methods and Techniques
  - o Descriptive Statistics
  - o Probability distributions
  - o Statistical tests
- Libraries for Statistical Analysis
- Determining Relationships between Variables
- Making Predictions about Future Events

Introduction to Statistical Analysis

Statistical analysis is the technique used to **extract meaningful hidden insights from the data that cannot be obtained using EDA**. It uses techniques like statistical testing to **analyze the data, determine relationships using variables, and also make predictions**. In this chapter, we will explore the **various statistical tests, distributions, and descriptive statistics** to explain the concepts of statistical analysis and also demonstrate the use of code snippets to understand problem-solving in real life.

Importance of Statistical Analysis

Statistical analysis is being used in various domains ranging from healthcare, transportation, legal, supply chain, finance, social sciences, defense, technology, manufacturing, insurance, marketing, and so on. It helps in data-driven decisions by making use of hidden insights, various statistical testing methods, and predictive modeling. This way, better decisions can be made along with optimization of the complex workflow.

Statistical Analysis Workflow

It is the systematic process of analyzing data using various statistical techniques so that the results can be communicated to the stakeholders for further decision-making. The steps are as follows:

Data Exploration

The data needs exploration for exploring the various data distributions, identifying outliers, and detecting missing values. Then the results can be communicated using various charts, plots, and graphs for better communication. These include box plots, violin plots, histograms, scatter plots, pie charts, and so on.

Variable Selection

Based on the problem definition at hand, it is imperative to identify the relevant variables for analysis. This can be identifying the **dependent variable** and **the independent variables** and also eliminating the non-essential variables. This way, one can understand whether the independent variables are correct enough to influence the dependent variable. This also helps to understand the complex modeling the variables are involved in, like the relationship between each other.

Statistical Tests

Statistical tests are imperative to analyzing variable relationships and drawing insights from them. There are tests like **t-tests, chi-square tests, correlation tests, analysis of variance (ANOVA), regression analysis, AD Fuller test**, and so on, that are used based on the type of data and the problem that needs to be solved. These tests help to understand the variable relationships, assess the statistical significance, and validate hypotheses.

Interpretation of Results

The statistical tests when performed output results like p-values, confidence intervals, statistical measures, test results, and so on, to help with insightful decision-making for solving business problems. The tests performed depend on the kind of problem one is solving.

Reporting and Visualization

The statistical analysis results must be communicated seamlessly with the help of reports and visualizations. This includes various charts, plots, tables, and graphs, along with providing clear explanations. There are pie charts, histograms, heat maps, line charts, bar charts, violin plots, box plots, and so on to help with a proper understanding of the data and the insights.

Statistical Methods and Techniques

Statistical analysis is the backbone of data analysis and helps to make informed decisions to solve business problems. There are descriptive statistics and inferential statistics. Parametric and non-parametric methods are also used. To proceed forward, we will be using a **dataset of all the countries in the world in 2023 (https://www.kaggle.com/datasets/nelgiriyewithana/countries-of-the-world-2023?select=world-data-2023.csv)**. It contains variables like `population`, `population density`, `unemployment rate`, `GDP`, `GDP per capita`, `forest cover in percentage`, `birth rate`, `fertility rate`, `infant mortality rate`, and so on.

We will load the data and do basic exploration in terms of missing value detection, identifying datatypes, and so on. The code is as follows:

```
import pandas as pd
import numpy as np


df = pd.read_csv('world-data-2023.csv')
df.head()
```

	Country	Density\n(P/Km2)	Abbreviation	Agricultural Land(%)	Land Area(Km2)	Armed Forces size	Birth Rate	Calling Code	Capital/Major City	Co2-Emissions	...	Out of pocket health expenditure	Physici thousa
0	Afghanistan	60	AF	58.10%	6.52.230	3,23.000	32.49	93.0	Kabul	8.672	...	78.40%	0
1	Albania	105	AL	43.10%	28,748	9,000	11.78	355.0	Tirana	4,536	...	56.90%	1
2	Algeria	18	DZ	17.40%	23,81,741	3,17,000	24.28	213.0	Algiers	1,50,006	...	28.10%	1
3	Andorra	164	AD	40.00%	468	NaN	7.20	376.0	Andorra la Vella	469	...	36.40%	3
4	Angola	26	AO	47.50%	12,46,700	1,17.000	40.73	244.0	Luanda	34,693	...	33.40%	0

Figure 5.1: *Top 5 rows of the dataset*

```
df.dtypes
```

```
Country                                           object
Density\n(P/Km2)                                  object
Abbreviation                                      object
Agricultural Land( %)                             object
Land Area(Km2)                                    object
Armed Forces size                                 object
Birth Rate                                       float64
Calling Code                                     float64
Capital/Major City                                object
Co2-Emissions                                     object
CPI                                               object
CPI Change (%)                                    object
Currency-Code                                     object
Fertility Rate                                   float64
Forested Area (%)                                 object
Gasoline Price                                    object
GDP                                               object
Gross primary education enrollment (%)            object
Gross tertiary education enrollment (%)           object
Infant mortality                                 float64
Largest city                                      object
Life expectancy                                  float64
Maternal mortality ratio                         float64
Minimum wage                                      object
Official language                                 object
Out of pocket health expenditure                  object
Physicians per thousand                          float64
Population                                        object
Population: Labor force participation (%)         object
Tax revenue (%)                                   object
Total tax rate                                    object
Unemployment rate                                 object
Urban_population                                  object
Latitude                                         float64
Longitude                                        float64
```

Figure 5.2: *The datatypes of the dataset*

Most of the variables are object datatypes and thus we need to convert them to float-type variables.

```
columns = ['Land Area(Km2)','Agricultural Land( %)','Armed Forces size',
'Population', 'Urban_population', 'Co2-Emissions', 'CPI Change (%)',
'Forested Area (%)', 'Gasoline Price','GDP', 'Gross primary education
enrollment (%)','Gross tertiary education enrollment (%)','Minimum
wage','Total tax rate', 'Unemployment rate', 'Out of pocket health ex-
penditure','Population: Labor force participation (%)']


for col in columns:
    df[col] = df[col].str.replace(',', '')
    df[col] = df[col].str.replace('$', '')
    df[col] = df[col].str.replace('%', '')
```

```
for col in columns:
    df[col] = pd.to_numeric(df[col])
```

The datatypes are converted into float data types. In the original dataset, there are **commas, percent signs, and dollar signs**, that need to be removed. Here, after the operation, the **data types are all in float format**.

Then we drop irrelevant columns as follows:

```
df.drop(columns=['Latitude', 'Longitude', 'Calling Code'], inplace=True)
```

After this, we create a histogram to represent the data.

```
import matplotlib.pyplot as plt
import seaborn as sns


# Histogram
df.hist(bins=50, figsize=(20,15))
plt.show()
```

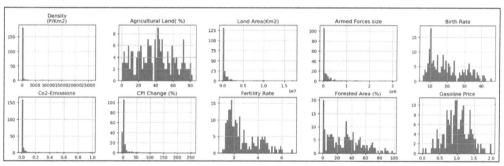

Figure 5.3: *The histogram representation of each variable of the dataset*

The histogram representation of each attribute of the dataset gives us a basic idea of each variable and how are they represented for each nation. Next, we will check the heatmap to understand the correlation between the variables.

```
f, ax = plt.subplots(figsize = (12,10))
sns.heatmap(df.loc[:, ['Land Area(Km2)','Agricultural Land( %)',
'Population',

                   'Urban_population', 'Co2-Emissions', 'Forested
Area(%)','GDP',

                   'Unemployment rate', 'Out of pocket health
expenditure','Population: Labor force participation (%)']].corr(),
```

```
        annot = True,
        linecolor = 'r',
        linewidths = .5,
        fmt = '.1f',
        ax = ax);
plt.show()
```

The goal of the correlation matrix or the heatmap is to identify the relation between the variables.

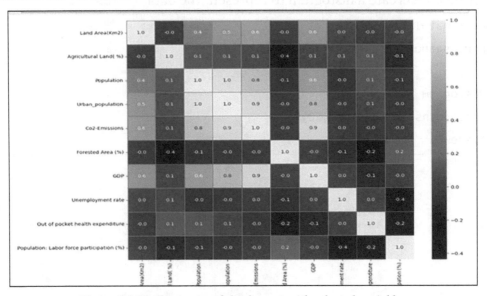

Figure 5.4: *The heat map of the dataset with selected variables*

From the preceding heatmap, we can find some **highly positive correlations** between **Urban population and carbon emissions, Urban population and GDP, Land Area, and GDP**, and some **negatively correlated variables** like the **forested area being negatively proportional to forested land**, the **Unemployment rate being negatively proportional to labor force participation**, and so on.

Descriptive Statistics

Descriptive statistics involves summarizing and describing the data using metrics like **mean, median, mode, variance,** and **standard deviation**. These statistics provide insights into the **central tendency, variability,** and **distribution of the data**. The following code uses the **.describe()** method to calculate the above metrics.

```
df.describe()
```

There are 23 relevant numeric float variables that have descriptive statistics.

	Agricultural Land(%)	Land Area(Km2)	Armed Forces size	Birth Rate	Co2- Emissions	CPI Change (%)	Fertility Rate	Forested Area (%)	Gasoline Price	GDP	...	Life expectancy
count	188.000000	1.940000e+02	1.710000e+02	189.000000	1.880000e+02	179.000000	188.000000	188.000000	175.000000	1.930000e+02	...	187.000000
mean	39.117553	6.896244e+05	1.592749e+05	20.214974	1.777992e+05	6.722346	2.698138	32.015426	1.002457	4.772959e+11	...	72.279679
std	21.783052	1.921609e+06	3.806288e+05	9.945774	8.387903e+05	24.450414	1.282267	23.791331	0.368858	2.172173e+12	...	7.483661
min	0.600000	0.000000e+00	0.000000e+00	5.900000	1.100000e+01	-4.300000	0.980000	0.000000	0.000000	4.727146e+07	...	52.800000
25%	21.700000	2.382825e+04	1.100000e+04	11.300000	2.304250e+03	1.000000	1.705000	11.000000	0.755000	8.454620e+09	...	67.000000
50%	39.600000	1.195110e+05	3.100000e+04	17.950000	1.230300e+04	2.300000	2.245000	32.000000	0.980000	3.438723e+10	...	73.200000
75%	55.375000	5.242560e+05	1.420000e+05	28.750000	6.388425e+04	4.250000	3.597500	48.175000	1.240000	2.340940e+11	...	77.500000
max	82.600000	1.709824e+07	3.031000e+06	46.080000	9.893038e+06	254.900000	6.910000	98.300000	2.000000	2.142770e+13	...	85.400000

8 rows × 23 columns

Figure 5.5: *The descriptive statistics of the dataset*

In the preceding table, we can observe the **minimum, maximum, mean, median (50th percentile), standard deviation, the 25th and 75th percentiles.** These values will make more sense if we correlate one variable with the other. For example, in the preceding heatmap, we found positively and negatively correlated variables although some variables did not correlate with any variable. For example, the maximum fertility rate recorded is 6.91 which is nearly 7 and the minimum is 1. Another example is the **median agricultural land in percentage is 39.6% and the maximum is 82.6%.**

Skewness

The asymmetry of a real-valued random variable's distribution that is centered on the mean is measured by its skewness. It measures how far the data points depart from the normal distribution, to put it simply. If we measure the skewness of all the float-type variables, we find that there are positive as well as negative values. If the skewness is less than zero, then the left tail of the curve is longer than the right tail, and if the skewness is greater than zero, then the data distribution of the right tail is longer than the left tail. If the skewness is zero, then the data is perfectly symmetrical and it is quite improbable to be a real-life data. Then **.skew()** method is used to find the skewness.

```
df.skew()
```

```
Agricultural Land( %)                              0.090844
Land Area(Km2)                                     5.569313
Armed Forces size                                  5.107848
Birth Rate                                         0.578672
Co2-Emissions                                      9.573513
CPI Change (%)                                     8.357341
Fertility Rate                                     0.947643
Forested Area (%)                                  0.518495
Gasoline Price                                     0.034371
GDP                                                8.578927
Gross primary education enrollment (%)            -0.995059
Gross tertiary education enrollment (%)            0.623984
Infant mortality                                   1.158554
Life expectancy                                   -0.528048
Maternal mortality ratio                           2.171510
Minimum wage                                       2.202087
Out of pocket health expenditure                   0.567070
Physicians per thousand                            1.007845
Population                                         8.390096
Population: Labor force participation (%)         -0.015166
Total tax rate                                     3.944664
Unemployment rate                                  1.356911
Urban_population                                   8.306802
dtype: float64
```

Figure 5.6: *The skewness index of the float type variables*

In positively skewed variables like **urban population, total tax rate, unemployment rate, minimum wage, population**, and so on, the mean is greater than the median, with a larger number of smaller values than fewer large values. The histogram plots of each variable are shown in *Figure* 5.7 for a better understanding of the skewness.

```
sns.histplot(df['Urban_population'])
plt.show()
```

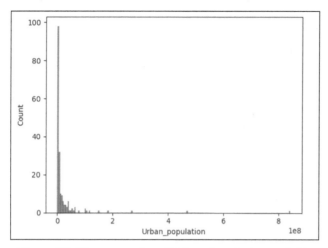

Figure 5.7: *Histogram plot of Urban Population variable*

The preceding plot is right-skewed, meaning most of the data is concentrated in the lower range.

```
sns.histplot(df['Total tax rate'])
plt.show()
```

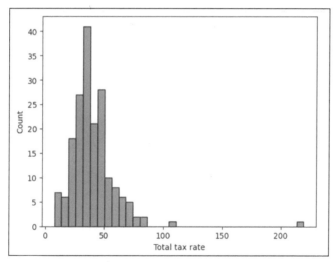

Figure 5.8: *Histogram plot of the Total tax rate variable*

The **Total tax rate** variable is also right-skewed as represented in the preceding plot.

```
sns.histplot(df['Unemployment rate'])
plt.show()
```

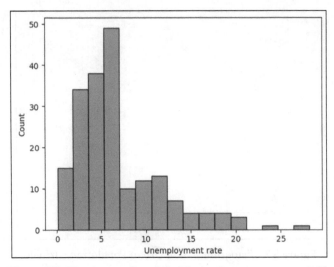

Figure 5.9: *Histogram plot of the Unemployment rate variable*

The **unemployment rate** of most nations is between the 2 and 12 percent range and is right skewed.

```
sns.histplot(df['Minimum wage'])
plt.show()
```

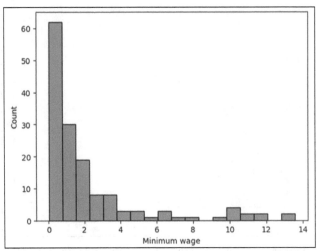

Figure 5.10: *Histogram plot of the Minimum wage variable*

The `minimum wage` of most nations lies between **1\$** and **3\$** and the data is right skewed.

```
sns.histplot(df['Population'])
plt.show()
```

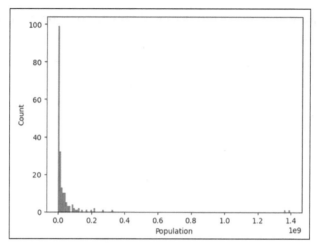

Figure 5.11: *Histogram plot of the Population variable*

Most nations have a **population below 200 million,** which is reflected in the preceding histogram and it is also right skewed.

The negatively skewed variables like `life expectancy` and `gross primary education enrollment (%)` have the data skewed to the left and the median is greater than the mean with a large number of larger values and fewer small values.

Some of the left-skewed variables are represented by histogram plots for better understanding.

```
sns.histplot(df['Life expectancy'])
plt.show()
```

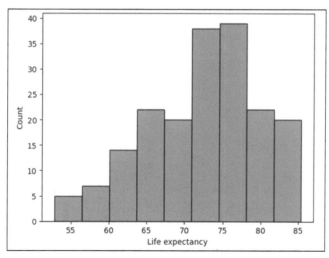

Figure 5.12: *Histogram plot of the Life Expectancy variable*

The **life expectancy** variable is left-skewed and almost **most of the nations live more than 70 years old**.

```
sns.histplot(df['Gross primary education enrollment (%)'])
plt.show()
```

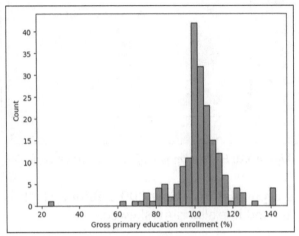

Figure 5.13: *Histogram plot of the Gross primary education enrollment (%) variable*

This Gross primary education enrollment percentage is also left-skewed.

Now there is the variable with symmetric distribution, that is, `labor force participation (%).`

```
sns.histplot(df['Population: Labor force participation (%)'])
plt.show()
```

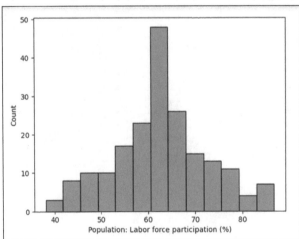

Figure 5.14: *Histogram plot of the Population: Labor Force Participation (%) variable*

The preceding plot shows an almost **symmetric distribution,** which shows that most of the nations maintain a **mean value of 60 to 65% of Labor force participation** in the market.

Kurtosis

Kurtosis can be defined as how different the tails of a distribution are from that of a normal distribution.

If the variables have **high kurtosis**, the distribution **has heavier tails and sharper peaks** than the normal distribution. It also means there are **more outliers in the variable**. This kind of kurtosis is called **leptokurtic**.

If the variables have **low kurtosis**, the distribution **has lighter tails and flatter peaks** than the normal distribution. There are also **fewer outliers in the variable** as compared to the former counterpart. This kind of kurtosis is called **platykurtic**.

The **mesokurtic** type variables have a **kurtosis value close to zero** or the same kurtosis as the normal distribution.

The following code uses `.kurtosis()` method to perform the operation.

```
df.kurtosis()
```

```
Agricultural Land( %)                          -0.947000
Land Area(Km2)                                 35.995016
Armed Forces size                              31.240094
Birth Rate                                     -0.821027
Co2-Emissions                                 102.748248
CPI Change (%)                                 76.336706
Fertility Rate                                 -0.044592
Forested Area (%)                              -0.451377
Gasoline Price                                 -0.001026
GDP                                            78.039315
Gross primary education enrollment (%)          7.967330
Gross tertiary education enrollment (%)        -0.503396
Infant mortality                                0.574173
Life expectancy                                -0.397122
Maternal mortality ratio                        4.871665
Minimum wage                                    4.243033
Out of pocket health expenditure               -0.323330
Physicians per thousand                         0.834057
Population                                     75.571246
Population: Labor force participation (%)      -0.306967
Total tax rate                                 30.931631
Unemployment rate                               1.880398
Urban_population                               81.149152
dtype: float64
```

Figure 5.15: The Kurtosis of the float type variables

We observe that there are a **lot of negative values meaning that they are platykurtic** and there are not a lot of outliers in the variables. Some have very **high values (leptokurtic)** and have **more outliers in them**.

Probability Distributions

Probability distributions are the mathematical functions that describe every possible value and likelihood that a random variable can take within a range. They are used to model a phenomenon to understand the probability estimates of an event being occurred.

There are two types of probability distribution namely **discrete and continuous**. **Discrete probability distributions** are also called **probability mass functions**, while **continuous probability distributions** are called **probability density functions**.

We will discuss some distributions like the **Normal distribution, Uniform distribution, Poisson distribution, Lambda distribution, Binomial distribution**, and so on.

Normal Distribution

Normal distribution is a symmetric curve and the shape is very similar to that of a bell, thus, sometimes it is also referred to as the **bell curve**.

The distribution of the **normal distribution is symmetric about the mean**, that is, half of the values fall below the mean, and half of the values are above the mean. The peak of the curve is **centered around the mean**, and **increasing the mean moves the curve to the right**, and **decreasing it moves the curve to the left**. The standard deviation is the spread of the data around the mean, that is, if the **standard deviation is small, the curve is steep**, and if the standard deviation is large there is a **larger spread and the curve is flat**.

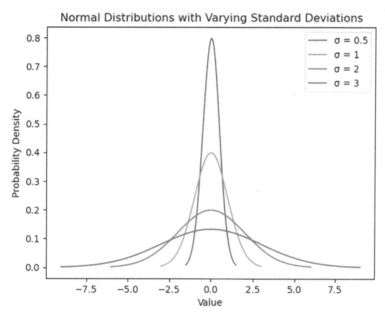

Figure 5.16: *Graphical representation for various standard deviation values*

In the preceding graph, we have various standard deviation values and we can see **that the higher the standard deviation value (represented by sigma), the wider and flatter the curve** in comparison to standard deviations that are lesser. The **less standard deviation values have steeper curves.**

The code for the normal distribution is as follows:

```
import matplotlib.pyplot as plt


data = np.random.normal(loc=0.0, scale=1.0, size=10000)
plt.hist(data, bins=30)
plt.show()
```

The preceding code uses the **numpy** library along with the **normal()** function with the number of data points as the size parameter, there are **30 bins used and a histogram** is created. The **matplotlib** library is used too.

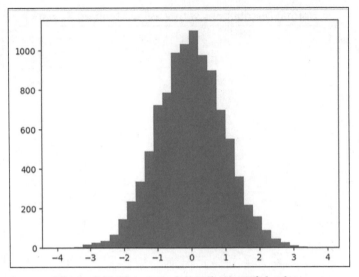

Figure 5.17: *The normal distribution of the data*

In the preceding distribution curve, we can see that the mean is at 0 and most of the data is centered around the mean. The curve is symmetric so there is **no skewness** and **most values cluster in the center around the mean**.

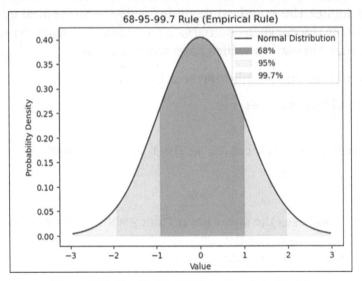

Figure 5.18: *The 68-95-99.7 Rule (Empirical Rule)*

The minimum and maximum values range from –3.5 (approximately) to 3.3 (approximately).

https://builtin.com/data-science/empirical-rule

Uniform Distribution

The uniform distribution defines an equal probability over a given range of continuous values. Here, it is mainly dependent on the minimum and maximum values in the distribution. The **mean = (a+b)/2**, where **a and b are the minimum and maximum values** respectively, the **variance = (b-a)^2/12**, the **distribution is symmetric** with the **majority of the values lying in the middle of the distribution**, and tails that decrease to the minimum and the maximum.

The code implementation is as follows:

```
from scipy.stats import uniform
# Generating random variables from Uniform distribution
data = uniform.rvs(size = 100000, loc = 5, scale=10)
```

```
# Plotting the results
sns.set_style('whitegrid')
sns.histplot(data, bins = 30, color = 'k')
plt.xlabel('interval')
plt.show()
```

The **scipy** library is used to import the **uniform** function. The **seaborn** library is used for visualizing the results using the **histogram** function.

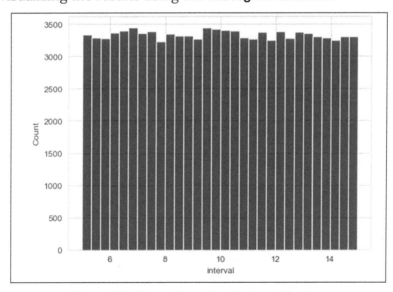

Figure 5.19: *The uniform distribution of the data*

The data ranges from 2 to 17 approximately and follows a symmetrical curve. It looks like a box if we try to **close the minimum and maximum values**.

It is used in the modeling of random variables with fixed likelihoods. If a random event has an equal chance of landing anywhere within a range, uniform distribution can be used to represent the probabilities of the possible outcomes.

Poisson Distribution

The `Poisson distribution` is a probability distribution that describes the number of times a particular event occurs in a fixed interval of time or space. The distribution is defined using a parameter called lambda, which is the expected number of occurrences during the observation.

It is used to model the events that occur independently at a constant rate, it can also be used to predict the probability of events occurring in a given time.

The code implementation is as follows:

```
from scipy.stats import poisson
data_poisson = poisson.rvs(mu=3, size=10000)
plt.hist(data_poisson, bins=30)
plt.show()
```

The **scipy** and the `matplotlib` libraries are used. The **Poisson** function is used in this case.

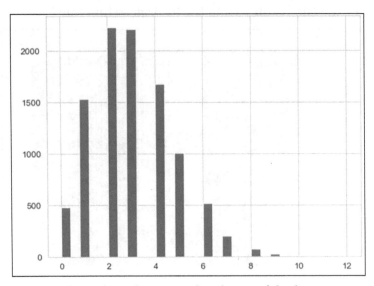

Figure 5.20: *The Poisson distribution of the data*

The preceding Poisson distribution shows the distribution of the data.

Lambda distribution

`Lambda distribution` is the exponential distribution curve here. The coding implementation is as follows:

```
from scipy.stats import expon
data_expon = expon.rvs(scale=1,loc=0,size=1000)
ax = sns.distplot(data_expon, kde=True, bins=100, color='skyblue', hist_
kws={"linewidth": 15,'alpha':1})
ax.set(xlabel='Exponential Distribution', ylabel='Frequency')
```

The **scipy** and the **seaborn** libraries are used. The **expon** function is used.

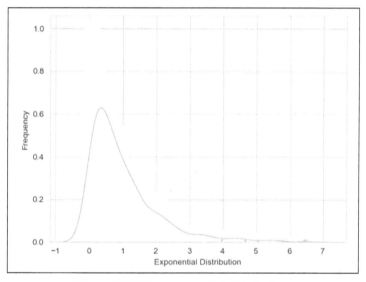

Figure 5.21: *The exponential distribution*

The data is generated using the **expon.rvs()** function with a **bin size of 100**.

Binomial distribution

A **binomial distribution** is one in which there are only two possible mutually exclusive outcomes, such as **success or failure, gain or loss, win or loss**, and where the probability of success and failure is the same across all trials.

The coding implementation is as follows:

```
from scipy.stats import binom
data_binom = binom.rvs(n=10,p=0.8,size=10000)
plt.hist(data_binom, bins=30)
plt.show()
```

The coding pattern is the same here as the previous distributions and we are using the `scipy` and the `matplotlib` libraries. The `binom` function is used with a **bin size of 30**.

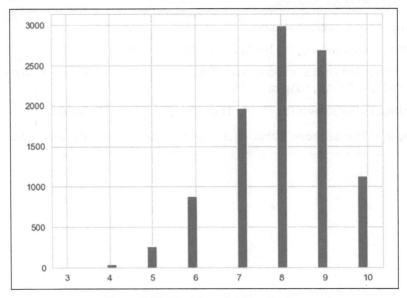

Figure 5.22: *The binomial distribution*

The binomial distribution in the preceding graph shows the frequency of the **trials from 1 to 10**. The **maximum frequency** is obtained at the **8th trial followed** by the **9th trial** and then the **7th trial**.

Statistical Tests

Statistical tests in statistical analysis in Python involve a variety of statistical tests to make informed decisions. Python has some libraries like `scipy.stats` and `statsmodels` that help in statistical testing. In the next sub-modules of statistical testing, we will work on some of the use cases based on the **countries' dataset** and understand the important features, like **Shapiro Wilk test, p-value, hypothesis testing, Analysis of Variance (ANOVA), Chi-square testing, t-test**, and so on.

Shapiro Wilk Test

We already have the data frame ready from the countries' dataset and calculate the **correlation between the variables labor force participation and unemployment rate**. The idea here is to understand the usage of the **Shapiro-Wilk test** using the use case. The coding implementation is as follows:

```
correlation = df['Unemployment rate'].corr(df['Population: Labor force
participation (%)'])
print('Correlation:', correlation)
```

```
Correlation: -0.4341421526724244
```

The preceding code shows the correlation between the variables and the **correlation coefficient** is **-0.43.**

The next code shows the usage of libraries **scipy** and **statsmodels** to perform the Shapiro-Wilk test.

```
import scipy.stats as stats
from scipy.stats import shapiro, pearsonr, ttest_ind, mannwhitneyu
from statsmodels.tsa.stattools import adfuller


# Normality Test for 'Unemployment rate'
stat, p = shapiro(df['Unemployment rate'])


print('Unemployment rate:', 'Statistics=%.2f, p=%.2f' % (stat, p))


if p > 0.05:
    print('Sample looks Gaussian')
else:
    print('Sample does not look Gaussian')
```

```
Result:
Unemployment rate: Statistics=0.87, p=0.00
Sample does not look Gaussian
```

The preceding code altogether imports the functions of **shapiro, pearsonr, ttest_ind, mannwhiteneyu** from the **scipy** library. The **statsmodels** library imports the **adfuller** function.

To understand the theory and conditions behind the Shapiro-Wilk test, it is performed by data scientists and statisticians to **check whether the data is**

normally distributed. The result returns a **statistic and a p-value**. The **p-value** is used to understand whether to **reject or accept the null hypothesis**. If the **p-value is low (typically < 0.05)**, then **we reject the null hypothesis and can conclude that the data is not normally distributed**, otherwise **if it is large**, then **we accept the null hypothesis** and can say that the **data is normally distributed**.

The result from the preceding code shows that the **p-value** is **1** and it is a **Gaussian (normally) distributed data**.

However, it is to be noted that the **p-value does not support the existence of an alternative hypothesis**. It only infers how likely the observed data has occurred under the null hypothesis. If we reject the null hypothesis, then **we cannot directly always support the alternate hypothesis**.

Hypothesis Testing

Hypothesis Testing is the statistical technique to conclude a population based on the sample data. It involves comparing the **two hypotheses**, namely the **null hypothesis (H0)** and **the alternative hypothesis (H1)**. For the Null Hypothesis (H0), there is no such significant difference or effect, on the contrary in the Alternative Hypothesis (H1), there are significant differences or effects.

There are these two errors namely, the **Type I** and **Type II** errors that occur in hypothesis testing.

The **Type I error** occurs when the **null hypothesis is rejected**, but it is true, meaning **it is a false positive situation**. Here, the machine learning **model predicts the output to be positive where it is negative**. The probability of making the **Type I error is alpha or the significance level**. It is the maximum acceptable probability of rejecting the null hypothesis when it is true. The significance level is **0.05** or **5%**.

When the **null hypothesis is not rejected but is true—a false negative situation— Type II error** occurs. In this case, the machine learning model forecasts a **negative output when a positive one exists. Beta represents the likelihood** of making a Type II error. A statistical test's power, which measures the likelihood of successfully rejecting the null hypothesis when it is false, is equal to 1 - beta. Researchers can increase the sample size or the significance level to lower the possibility of Type II mistakes.

One Sample t-test

The coding implementation for hypothesis testing (`One Sample t-test`) is as follows:

```
from scipy import stats


# One-sample t-test
t_statistic, p_value = stats.ttest_1samp(df['Unemployment rate'], 0.0)
print('t-statistic:', t_statistic)
print('p-value:', p_value)
```

```
Result:
t-statistic: 19.417670076487422
p-value: 2.32361093809253e-47
```

The **t-statistic value in a one-sample t-test** is measured by **how much the sample mean differs from the hypothesized population mean**. If the **t-statistic value is larger than the critical value** or the `p-value` < 0.05, then **we reject the null hypothesis**. On the contrary, if the **t-statistic value is less than the critical value** or the `p-value` > 0.05, then **we fail to reject the null hypothesis**. In this case, the `p-value` < 0.05, thus we reject the null hypothesis.

One sample independent t-test

The **independent sample t-test** is the parametric test that is used to compare the means of the two independent groups. It's used to test for a statistically significant difference in the means between the two groups. In this case, we create a **data frame with two groups** and certain scores. Then we **categorize the number in the two groups** and then perform the **independent t-test**.

```
df = pd.DataFrame({
    'group': ['A', 'A', 'A', 'A', 'A', 'B', 'B', 'B', 'B', 'B'],
    'score': [371, 542, 275, 389, 2145, 1459, 153, 874, 321, 525]
})
group_A = df[df['group'] == 'A']['score']
group_B = df[df['group'] == 'B']['score']


t_statistic, p_value = ttest_ind(group_A, group_B)
print('t-statistic:', t_statistic)
print('p-value:', p_value)
```

```
Result:
```

```
t-statistic: 0.18480230929708708
```

```
p-value: 0.8579830736566254
```

The p-value, in this case, is greater than 0.05, so we fail to reject the null hypothesis. The condition remains the same as the **1-sample t-test**.

Chi-Square test

The statistical test used to determine whether there is a significant relationship between two categorical variables is called the **Chi-Square test**. To compare observed data with expected data in accordance with particular hypotheses, it is used in hypothesis testing.

By contrasting the observed frequencies in each category of a contingency table with the frequencies we would anticipate if there were no link between the categories, the chi-square test statistic is generated.

The coding implementation is as follows:

```
#Chi-Square test using created dummy data


from scipy.stats import chi2_contingency


# Sample DataFrame
data = {'Rain': ['Yes', 'No', 'Yes', 'No', 'Yes', 'No', 'Yes'],
        'Temperature': ['High', 'Low', 'High', 'High', 'Low', 'Low',
'High']}
df1 = pd.DataFrame(data)
#print(df1)


contingency_table = pd.crosstab(df1['Rain'], df1['Temperature'])
chi2, p, dof, expected = chi2_contingency(contingency_table)
print('Chi-square statistic:', chi2)
print('p-value:', p)


Result obtained:
Chi-square statistic: 0.10937499999999994
p-value: 0.7408568142938687
```

The results have a **chi-square statistic** and a **p-value**. Here the **p-value >= 0.05,** thus we fail to reject the **null hypothesis and the variables rain and temperature are independent of each other** by using the chi-square test.

Analysis of Variance (ANOVA)

ANOVA is the **statistical method** used to test the differences between two or more means. ANOVA tests the hypothesis that the **means of two or more populations are equal**. ANOVAs assess the importance of one or more factors by comparing the response variable means at the different factor levels. The null hypothesis states that all the population means are equal while the alternative hypothesis states that at least one is different.

To perform ANOVA, the **scipy** library uses the **f_oneway** function, which performs a **1-way ANOVA**. The data frame with 2 groups of **A** and **B** are used.

```python
df = pd.DataFrame({
    'group': ['A', 'A', 'A', 'A', 'A', 'B', 'B', 'B', 'B', 'B'],
    'score': [371, 542, 275, 389, 2145, 1459, 153, 874, 321, 525]
})
group_A = df[df['group'] == 'A']['score']
group_B = df[df['group'] == 'B']['score']


fvalue, pvalue = stats.f_oneway(group_A , group_B)
print(fvalue, pvalue)
```

```
Result:
0.03415189352153622 0.8579830736566272
```

The main output statistic in ANOVA is the f-value. It is the ratio of the variability between groups to the variability within groups. A larger F-value indicates a greater difference between groups and suggests that the independent variable significantly affects the dependent variable. If the **p-value < 0.05**, then it is **unlikely that the observed differences among group means occurred by chance**, and the null hypothesis of no difference among group means can be rejected.

In the preceding code result, the **p-value > 0.05, meaning that the null hypothesis can be accepted.**

Regression Analysis

Regression Analysis is the statistical testing technique that helps us understand the relation between the **dependent variable and one or more independent variables**. The fundamental idea is to understand if the independent variables can predict the dependent variable. Let's use the code to understand the relevant output statistics involved.

```
import statsmodels.api as sm

X = sm.add_constant(df['Population: Labor force participation (%)']) #
adding a constant

model = sm.OLS(df['Unemployment rate'], X).fit()

print_model = model.summary()

print(print_model)
```

In the preceding code, we have tried to understand the relation between **labor force participation and the unemployment rate**. The `add_constant()` function is used here. The **OLS function (Ordinary Least Squares)** is used along with the **.fit()** method to create the model. The model summary is as follows:

```
                          OLS Regression Results
============================================================================
Dep. Variable:        Unemployment rate   R-squared:                      0.186
Model:                             OLS    Adj. R-squared:                 0.182
Method:                  Least Squares    F-statistic:                    44.14
Date:                 Wed, 30 Aug 2023    Prob (F-statistic):          3.05e-10
Time:                        19:47:25    Log-Likelihood:               -563.83
No. Observations:                 195    AIC:                            1132.
Df Residuals:                     193    BIC:                            1138.
Df Model:                           1
Covariance Type:            nonrobust
============================================================================
                                            coef    std err      t    P>|t|    [0.025    0.975]
----------------------------------------------------------------------------
const                                     19.8782    2.003    9.926    0.000    15.928    23.828
Population: Labor force participation (%)  -0.2095   0.032   -6.643    0.000    -0.272    -0.147
============================================================================
Omnibus:                       78.547    Durbin-Watson:                  1.896
Prob(Omnibus):                  0.000    Jarque-Bera (JB):             222.298
Skew:                           1.740    Prob(JB):                     5.35e-49
Kurtosis:                       6.904    Cond. No.                        405.
============================================================================

Notes:
[1] Standard Errors assume that the covariance matrix of the errors is correctly specified.
```

Figure 5.23: The Regression model summary

The output statistics are **R-squared, f-statistic, log-likelihood, coefficients, p-value, and adjusted r-squared**. The output statistics are defined as follows:

- **The Coefficients:** The coefficients, in this case, are the **constant** and the **labor force participation(independent variable)** that represent the change in the **dependent variable (unemployment rate)** for a change of one unit in the independent variable, assuming that all the other variables are constant. If the **coefficient is statistically significant (p-value < 0.05)**, the variable can be called a **good predictor in the model**.

- **The t-statistic:** This value is calculated by the **coefficient divided by its standard error**. A **larger value of the t-statistic proves that it is against the null hypothesis** (that is, the coefficient is zero, or the independent variable has zero to no effect on the dependent variable).

- **The p-value:** A small p-value (typically < 0.05) proves that there is **evidence against the null hypothesis** and also suggests that the **independent variable (labor force participation)** is a good predictor in the model.

- **The F-statistic:** This number evaluates the regression model's overall significance. It contrasts a model **with no predictor variables with the actual model**. The **null hypothesis is refuted** (that is, the **model without predictors fits the data as well as the full model**) if the p-value for the **F-statistic is low (<0.05)**, indicating that at least one of the predictors is strongly related to the dependent variable.

- **The R-squared statistic:** The **R-squared statistic** illustrates the **percentage of the dependent variable's variance** that can be accounted for by the independent variables. If the **R-squared value is close to 1**, the model **likely accounts for a sizable proportion of the variance in the dependent variable**.

Adfuller test statistic

The **Augmented Dickey-Fuller (ADF) test** is the statistical test to determine whether a given time series is stationary, we will explore more on this in *Chapter 6: Time Series Analysis*. The ADF test statistic is a negative number if it is more on the negative side, then there is a higher probability of null hypothesis rejection, and there is a higher probability that the time series is stationary. The coding implementation is as follows:

```
result = adfuller(df['Population: Labor force participation (%)'])

print('ADF Statistic: %f' % result[0])
print('p-value: %f' % result[1])

ADF Statistic: -7.525260
p-value: 0.000000
```

The **adfuller** function is derived from the **statsmodels** library. There are the **ADF statistic** and the **p-value**. The **p-value <0.05**, meaning the null hypothesis is rejected in this case.

Libraries for Statistical Analysis

The libraries in statistical analysis are an inbuilt set of functions that the user can use to do deeper data analysis. There are pre-written codes to perform tasks. The relevant libraries used for statistical analysis are **Pandas, Numpy, scipy, statsmodel, scikit-learn, PyMC3, Pingouin, and PyStan**. Since we have used **Pandas** and **Numpy** frequently in the previous chapters and also in this chapter, we will not be discussing this, instead, we will discuss a little about the other libraries.

Scipy

The Scipy library is built on Numpy by offering more statistical and scientific features. It is useful for sophisticated statistical analysis since it has modules for **optimization (`scipy.optimize`), statistical functions (`scipy.stats`), interpolation(`scipy.interpolate`), signal processing, linear algebra functions (`scipy.linalg`), file input/output (`scipy.io`), and some special functions (`scipy.special`)**.

Statsmodels

Statsmodels is the complete library for statistical modeling and testing. It provides a wide range of statistical functionalities, such as **ordinary least squares (`sm.ols()`), function to fit the model to the data (`model.fit()`), getting the summary of the results after fitting the model (`results.model()`), cross-correlation function (`smt.ccf()`)**, and so on, to name a few. Additionally, it offers capabilities for model visualization and diagnostics.

Scikit-learn

Scikit-learn is a machine-learning library that also has statistical functions under its belt. These include functions like **`train_test_split()`** which is used to split the datasets between train and test datasets, **`model.fit()`** to fit the model to the data, **`model.predict()`** to predict the target for the provided data, **`model.score()`** that calculates the mean accuracy on the given test data and labels for classification algorithms, **`GridSearchCV()`** for hyper-parameter tuning to make the model performance better, **`cross_val_score()`** to calculate the cross-validation score by dividing the dataset k times and then training and testing the model k times, and **`confusion_matrix()`** to find the classification mismatches in the final result, thereby assessing the model performance.

PyMC3

PyMC3 is a **probabilistic programming library** that supports **Bayesian analysis**. It allows for flexible specification of probabilistic models and performs Bayesian inference using **Markov Chain Monte Carlo (MCMC)** sampling. PyMC3 enables the estimation of posterior distributions and uncertainty quantification. Some of the functions used are as follows:

- `pm.Model()` is used to instantiate the model,
- `pm.Normal()` is used to create a normal random variable,
- `pm.HalfNormal()` is used to define **Half Normal random variable**,
- `pm.sample()` is used to draw samples from the posterior using **MCMC,**
- `pm.traceplot()` is used to plot the posterior distributions and sample paths of the model parameters,
- `pm.summary()` is used to create a text-based output of common posterior statistics.

https://sjster.github.io/introduction_to_computational_statistics/docs/Production/PyMC3.html

Pingouin

Pingouin is a statistical package written in Python 3 and is based on Pandas and Numpy. It does simple and complex statistical operations and is also used mostly for detailed statistical output in comparison to that of `scipy` and `statsmodels`. Some of the statistical functions used in Pingouin are `pg.ttest()` that gives the output of **T-value, p-value, degrees of freedom, effect size (Cohen's d), statistical power, and Bayes Factor (BF10), Analysis of Variance (ANOVA)** where the `dframe.anova()` function is used, `dframe.pairwise_corr()` for **pairwise correlation, partial correlation** where `dframe.pcorr()` function is used, testing the **normality of the data** using the `.normality()` function.

PyStan

Stan, a tool for Bayesian inference, has a Python interface called **PyStan**. Stan is a cutting-edge framework for **high-performance statistical computation and statistical modeling**. In numerous domains of social, engineering, and business, PyStan is used for **statistical modeling, data analysis, and prediction**. Some of the functions used are `StanModel()` which is used to compile a Stan Model, the `sampling()` function is used to draw samples from the model, the `extract()` function is used to extract samples from the fit object, `to_frame()` function is used to convert the fit object into a pandas data frame, and the `build()` function is used to build a Stan model.

These libraries provide a plethora of tools and functions to support **various aspects of statistical analysis**. They simplify the implementation of **statistical methods, offer efficient computation**, and **enhance the exploration and understanding of data**. By leveraging these libraries, **analysts and data scientists can perform robust statistical analysis and derive meaningful insights from data**.

Determining Relationships between Variables

The statistical analysis helps to determine the relationships between the variables. There are correlations and dependencies between the variables to understand how they interact and affect each other. There are correlation analyses, regression analyses, and various hypothesis testing techniques to understand the significance of the relationships.

In **correlation analysis**, we understand how directly or indirectly variables are related to each other along with the strength of the relation. There can be a **high positive correlation between the numeric variables, a high negative correlation between the variables,** or **no relation** at all between them.

Finding the relationship between a target variable and one or more independent variables is aided by **regression analysis**. It enables us to comprehend the effects of **altering the independent factors on the dependent variable**. Regression analysis helps **predict the dependent variable, identify errors between the expected and observed values of the target variable, and examine the direction and strength of correlations**.

When examining connections between categorical variables and a continuous dependent variable, **ANOVA** is used. It aids in determining whether there are any notable differences in the **dependent variable's means across several categories of the independent variable**. ANOVA helps determine which groups are **statistically different from one another and sheds light on the influence of categorical factors**.

Using one of these tests can also help in **determining the relevant and irrelevant features from the data by comparing the relationship between the variables**. Multicollinear features can be removed.

Making Predictions about Future Events

Statistical analysis helps us to make future predictions based on historical data and the extracted patterns. These involve using **predictive modeling**

techniques, and statistical algorithms to predict future events. There are **time series analysis, regression analysis, and machine learning algorithms** to do predictive modeling.

Time series analysis is used to **forecast events based on historical temporal data**. It uses **trends, seasonalities, causalities**, and so on to make accurate predictions. There are algorithms like **ARIMA, SARIMA, exponential smoothing, LSTM**, and so on to do the forecasting. This is very much used in the financial domain to predict the price of stocks in the future and plan to invest in those stocks. In the sales domain, the companies try to forecast sales numbers to plan investments for the future. In this way, they can focus not only on their products but also on attracting new customers and retaining old ones. There can be a plethora of applications for time series forecasting that we can explore more in the next chapter.

Regression analysis as discussed earlier, examines the relation between independent variables and the target variable. There are parameters of the regression model that can be tuned to attain the predicted values of the dependent variable. This way, we can forecast events based on historical data.

Supervised, unsupervised, semi-supervised, and reinforcement-based algorithms are the different categories of **machine learning algorithms**. We deal with a variety of algorithms used in predictive modeling, including **xgboost, neural networks, decision trees, random forests, and logistic regression**. These algorithms discover patterns and relationships from the training data to predict or categorize based on the unseen test data.

Conclusion

Statistical data analysis is a vast field, and this chapter covered various **statistical testing techniques and distributions** using a use case on a **country dataset**. It also explained some of the **relevant statistics-based libraries and functions** that are used in the industry today. We need to explore, dig deeper, and play with various kinds of real-world datasets to improve **our statistical testing skills and build a solid foundation**. Happy Analyzing!

This concludes the chapter on *Statistical Data Analysis*. In the next chapter, we will understand and explore temporal data to predict future events. We will learn the concepts of **trends, seasonality, causality,** and practice with various algorithms, and do **comparative analysis between them**. Moreover, there are also **performance metrics** that help to examine the performance of the **time series models and which algorithms perform better than the others** in that situation. We will use a real-life use case to do the operations.

References

- Normal distribution reference: https://numpy.org/doc/stable/reference/random/generated/numpy.random.normal.html
- Uniform distribution reference: https://sid-sharma1990.medium.com/probability-distributions-1-uniform-distribution-f75cd22ebf0a
- Poisson distribution reference: https://medium.com/@snehabajaj108/the-poisson-exponential-distribution-using-python-2e9959fdcbc7
- Lambda distribution reference:
  - https://www.datacamp.com/tutorial/probability-distributions-python
  - https://medium.datadriveninvestor.com/mathematics-for-machine-learning-part-5-8df72392ec10
- Binomial distribution:
  - https://github.com/mandliya/ml/blob/master/maths/Probability/Probability.ipynb

https://stackoverflow.com/questions/69290701/difference-between-scipy-stats-binom-and-np-random-binomial

Keywords

Statistical analysis, Variable transformation, variable selection, statistical tests, data visualizations, skewness, histogram, probability distributions, normal distribution, Hypothesis testing, ANOVA, t-test, chi-square, one sample t-test, regression, statsmodels, scipy

## CHAPTER 6

Time Series Analysis and Forecasting

Introduction

The field of *Time Series Analysis and Forecasting* is crucial in understanding and predicting the patterns in temporal data. In this chapter, we explore the concepts and techniques, starting from the concepts of **stationarity, autocorrelations, partial autocorrelations, residuals, seasonality, trends**, and other important algorithms. We will look into time series data and explore the various algorithms of **Auto-Regressive (AR), ARIMA, SARIMA, FBprophet, and LSTM (Long Short Term Memory)**, and perform comparative analysis on the same. There are also performance metrics like **Mean Squared Error (MSE), Root Mean Squared Error (RMSE), Mean Absolute Error (MAE)** and so on, that we will use to compare the models. There are some **real-life use cases like sales data, stock data, and weather data** to connect how real-life time series forecasting works.

Structure

In this chapter, we will discuss the following topics:

- Understanding Time Series Analysis and Forecasting
- Importance of Time Series Analysis and Forecasting
- Time Series Analysis
  - Types of Time Series Data
  - Stationarity and Non-Stationarity
  - Trend, Seasonality, and Noise
  - Autocorrelation and Partial Autocorrelation

- o White Noise
- o Visualizing Time Series Data
- Time Series Forecasting
  - o Simple moving average
  - o Exponential Smoothing
  - o Autoregressive (AR)
  - o ARIMA
  - o FbProphet
  - o Deep Learning for Time Series Forecasting (CNN and LSTM)
- Evaluation of Time Series Forecasting Models
  - o Exploring the parameters in the models
  - o Performance Metrics of the models to Measure their accuracy
- Auto Time Series Libraries

Understanding Time Series Analysis and Forecasting

Time series analysis is the statistical technique that deals with temporal or trend analysis. It provides an extra source of information and dependencies between the data. It can be applied to **stock market analysis, economic forecasting, sales forecasting analysis, weather forecasting, and budgetary analysis,** to name a few. There are **linear regression models and autoregressive integrated moving average (ARIMA) models** that are mostly used for forecasting the relevant data. The ARIMA models utilize past data to make future predictions. There are various **hidden trends and patterns such as seasonalities, trends, and lags** that help exploit the data so that more inferences can be drawn, thus making it easier to forecast results.

Time series analysis helps us to understand the reason behind the **specific behaviors of the data**, on the other hand, **forecasting** helps to understand what can **happen in the future considering the past data is present with us**. For example, from the sales data in the time domain, we can infer what products are bought more, which products are bought in bundles, how the users buy during the festival seasons such as clothes and accessories or only clothes and fewer accessories, and so on. This paves the way for time series forecasting where the data analysts and data scientists predict which pattern the buyers will follow in the next season in buying the products, which products will likely be sold more and which of them will be sold less, and so on.

In this chapter, we will dig deep into various underlying patterns in the data and explore them with various **time series modeling techniques**. We will also utilize some **auto time series Python libraries** to proceed forward with the use cases.

Importance of Time Series Analysis and Forecasting

Time series analysis and forecasting are important in various fields like **finance, insurance, social sciences, supply chain**, **climate change**, and so on. Intelligent decision-making and strategic planning are the causes of perfect analysis and forecasting. Whether it's **predicting future sales for a particular store or company**, stock market forecasting, or forecasting weather-related activities, forecasting, and time series analysis are extremely essential.

Time series analysis and forecasting also help understand and model dynamic systems. Time series models capture the temporal dependencies in the data, thus **describing, explaining, and predicting the dynamics** of the system. These models help us understand the system's behavior and its response to various factors.

In conclusion, time series analysis and forecasting are powerful tools for understanding and predicting temporal data. They provide valuable insights into the **patterns, trends, and dynamics in the data**, which are crucial for intelligent decision-making and strategic planning. As the volume and complexity of time series data continue to grow, the importance of time series analysis and forecasting will only increase.

Time Series Analysis

There are various features based on which we can do time series analysis such as whether the **data is stationary, understanding the trend, seasonality, and noise in the data, autocorrelation, white noise**, and also **visualizing the time series data**. These attributes are essential while we are trying to explore time series data and give us hidden patterns and insights that are impossible to search by usual methods.

Types of Time Series Data

Time series data can be classified based on the type of observations and the regularity of time intervals. The different types of time series data are as follows:

- **Univariate Time Series Data:** This type of data has single (variable) observations that are recorded temporally. A perfect example of this can be the daily sales data recordings of a particular product in a store.

- **Multivariate Time Series Data:** In this kind of data as the name suggests, multiple attributes are at play. The present data is dependent on the past data as well as on other variables. For example, the sales data of the particular product, sales data of some correlated product, like if a person buys a cricket bat, then he/she is also likely to buy cricket balls, wickets, the guards worn by batsmen, and so on. This can also be exemplified considering seasonal data, where customers buy certain products depending on some festival at a particular time of the year. The customer buys multiple products on a certain occasion.

- **Continuous Time Series Data:** This type of data has continuous recordings with the time variable at continuous intervals. For example, tracking the stock market data of a particular company.

- **Discrete-Time Series Data:** There are data points at distinct points of time. For instance, the daily temperature data at specific hours of the day.

- **Regular and Irregular Time Series Data:** For regular time series data, the observation points are recorded at regular intervals like every 30 minutes, every hour, or daily or weekly. For irregular time series data, the observation data points are recorded at random or irregular time intervals. For instance, if earthquakes are happening, then the data points are recorded at random time intervals.

- **Event time series data:** The event time series data is based on specific events where the data points are recorded at time stamps where an event occurs. For example, earthquake data or data from the buying of products at a particular festival.

- **Metric Time Series:** The data points are collected based on metrics at regular time intervals. For example, the CPU utilization of a system measured every second forms a metric time series.

- **Panel data:** In panel data, which can also refer to longitudinal or cross-sectional time series data, several entities are observed across time. For instance, panel data is created using the daily closing prices of all S&P 500 businesses throughout the year.

- **Wide format:** In this data format, each variable has a separate column, and each row relates to a time stamp. In this case, the number of variables is smaller in number.

- **Long format:** In this data format, there are a lot of rows with many variables. Each observation is represented by a single unique row and there are separate columns for timestamp, entity, and other variable values.

In the next subsections, we will explore the concepts of stationarity, autocorrelation, partial autocorrelation, seasonality, trend, white noise, and tests like the Augmented Dickey-Fuller (ADF) test to test the stationarity in a time series data.

Stationarity and Non-Stationarity

A **stationary** time series is one whose statistical properties such as **mean, variance, autocorrelation**, and so on, stay constant over time.

- **Strong stationarity:** This stochastic process' unconditional joint probability distribution does not alter as time goes on in the process. As a result, variables like mean and variance also remain constant over time. For instance, if we take any two parts from the time series, they should have the same distribution.

- **Weak stationarity:** When a process exhibits **weak stationarity**, the **mean, variance, and autocorrelation remain consistent throughout time**. For weakly stationary time series, the daily changes in stock price data can be considered. The actual prices may fluctuate, but the **changes or returns** from **one day to the next may have a constant mean and variance.**

Non-stationary series that rely on time have too many parameters to take into consideration while modeling the time series, hence stationarity is crucial. A non-stationary series can be readily transformed into a stationary series using the `diff()` function.

On the contrary, **non-stationarity** refers to a time series where these statistical properties vary with time.

To check whether a given time series is stationary or not, there are several methods, including:

- **Visual inspection:** Plotting the time series data and visually examining it for **trends, seasonality, or changes in statistical properties over time**. This can involve plotting the series itself, the **rolling mean, or the autocorrelation function (ACF).**

- **Augmented Dickey-Fuller (ADF) test:** The **ADF test** is a statistical analysis that determines **whether a time series contains a unit root**, which denotes non-stationarity. It contrasts the **alternative hypothesis of stationarity with the null hypothesis that the time series** has a **unit root and is therefore non-stationary.** The **null hypothesis is rejected and stationarity is indicated** if the **test statistic is smaller than the crucial value**. This test was already shown in *Chapter 5: Statistical Analysis*.

Before we deep dive into the ADF test and analysis of the individual parameters and output values, let's understand a bit about the dataset. The dataset was used from the UC Irvine data repository (https://archive.ics.uci.edu/dataset/360/air+quality). It has **hourly responses that are recorded using a multisensor device for an Italian city**. The data is present in an Excel format. We convert it into a data frame. The top of the data looks somewhat as shown in *Figure 6.1*. The data were recorded from March 2004 to February 2005 to measure the air quality using chemical sensor devices. The average concentrations of CO, Non-Metanic Hydrocarbons, Benzene, Total Nitrogen Oxides (NOx), and Nitrogen Dioxide (NO$_2$) were recorded.

	Date	Time	CO(GT)	PT08.S1(CO)	NMHC(GT)	C6H6(GT)	PT08.S2(NMHC)	NOx(GT)	PT08.S3(NOx)	NO2(GT)	PT08.S4(NO2)	PT08.S5(O3)	
0	2004-03-10	18:00:00	2.6	1360.00	150	11.881723	1045.50	166.0	1056.25	113.0	1692.00	1267.50	1
1	2004-03-10	19:00:00	2.0	1292.25	112	9.397165	954.75	103.0	1173.75	92.0	1558.75	972.25	1
2	2004-03-10	20:00:00	2.2	1402.00	88	8.997817	939.25	131.0	1140.00	114.0	1554.50	1074.00	1
3	2004-03-10	21:00:00	2.2	1375.50	80	9.228796	948.25	172.0	1092.00	122.0	1583.75	1203.25	1
4	2004-03-10	22:00:00	1.6	1272.25	51	6.518224	835.50	131.0	1205.00	116.0	1490.00	1110.00	1

Figure 6.1: *Top five rows of the data frame*

The **date and time stamp variables are merged** and then converted to **datetime datatype.**

```
df['DateTime'] = df['Date'].astype(str) + ' ' + df['Time'].astype(str)
df['DateTime'] = pd.to_datetime(df['DateTime'])


#transforming DateTime column into index
df = df.set_index('DateTime')
```

	Date	Time	CO(GT)	PT08.S1(CO)	NMHC(GT)	C6H6(GT)	PT08.S2(NMHC)	NOx(GT)	PT08.S3(NOx)	NO2(GT)	PT08.S4(NO2)	PT08.S5(O3)	
0	2004-03-10	18:00:00	2.6	1360.00	150	11.881723	1045.50	166.0	1056.25	113.0	1692.00	1267.50	1
1	2004-03-10	19:00:00	2.0	1292.25	112	9.397165	954.75	103.0	1173.75	92.0	1558.75	972.25	1
2	2004-03-10	20:00:00	2.2	1402.00	88	8.997817	939.25	131.0	1140.00	114.0	1554.50	1074.00	1
3	2004-03-10	21:00:00	2.2	1375.50	80	9.228796	948.25	172.0	1092.00	122.0	1583.75	1203.25	1
4	2004-03-10	22:00:00	1.6	1272.25	51	6.518224	835.50	131.0	1205.00	116.0	1490.00	1110.00	1

Figure 6.2: *The transformed data with the date time column as the index*

The preceding screenshot shows the transformed data into the **datetime data type** and also as the index for better data analysis, and forecasting later.

Now we will explore the code snippet of the **ADF test using Python**. The **statsmodels** package is used to import the **adfuller** function.

```
from statsmodels.tsa.stattools import adfuller


# Perform Augmented Dickey-Fuller test
result = adfuller(df["NO2(GT)"])


# Extract the p-value from the test result
p_value = result[1]


# Check if the series is stationary based on the p-value
if p_value < 0.05:
    print("The time series is stationary.")
else:
    print("The time series is non-stationary.")
```

The **data frame is df** and the **NO2(GT)** is the variable of recordings of the **Nitrogen Dioxide** gas. We will be using the p-value testing technique to infer whether the data is stationary or not. In this case, the **p-value < 0.05**, which states that the **null hypothesis can be rejected**, inferring that the **NO2(GT) data is stationary**.

Trend, Seasonality, and Noise

Seasonality in time series refers to the changes in a year that happen during certain regular intervals. Any predictable pattern that **happens over 1 year can be called seasonal**. Seasonality happens in different types of datasets in the **e-commerce domain, sales domain, finance stock prices domain, transportation domain, climate change domain**, and so on. Seasonality can be **additive and multiplicative**. In **additive seasonality**, the changes over time are of the same magnitude, in absolute terms. In **multiplicative seasonality**, the changes increase or decrease over time.

machinelearningmastery.com (https://machinelearningmastery.com/)

There are three components of a time series that are **seasonality, trend, and residuals**. These can be found using the **seasonal_decompose()** function from the **statsmodels** library. The code snippet for the seasonality, trend, and residual is as follows:

```
from statsmodels.tsa.seasonal import seasonal_decompose


# assuming 'df' is your DataFrame and 'time_series_column' is the column
with the time series data


decomposed = seasonal_decompose(df['NO2(GT)'],model='additive', extrapo-
late_trend='freq', period=1)
decomposed.plot()
plt.show()


#https://analyticsindiamag.com/why-decompose-a-time-series-and-how/


trend = decomposed.trend
seasonal = decomposed.seasonal
residual = decomposed.resid
```

The **seasonal_decompose()** function is used and the **additive seasonality** is used meaning the changes over time are of the same magnitude, in absolute terms. In **multiplicative sseasonality**, the changes increase or decrease over time. All the plots are shown as follows:

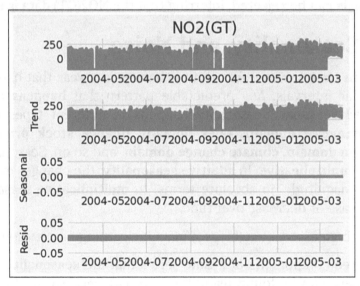

Figure 6.3: *The seasonality, trend, and residual plots of the data*

All the plots of observed values, seasonality, trend, and residuals are shown in *Figure* 6.3. We can also observe individual plots with the code snippet as follows:

```
level = decomposed.observed
level.plot();
```

The observed values of the **NO2(GT)** variable are visualized as follows.

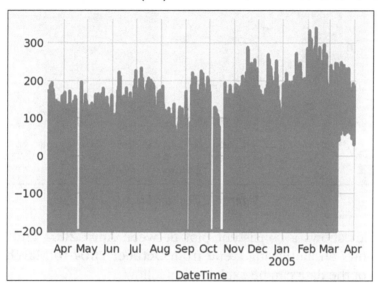

Figure 6.4: *The observed value plot*

The trend in a time series data is the increasing or decreasing patterns. It may be understood by the **increasing buying patterns trend during festival seasons and decreasing patterns trend during normal seasons**. Also, if we try to correlate with the example of air quality levels for the Italian city, we can see that the NO2 levels are at an **increasing trend from November 2004 to March 2005**. The code snippet is as follows:

```
trend=decomposed.trend
trend.plot();
```

The **trend** object is used to find the **trend of the time series data**.

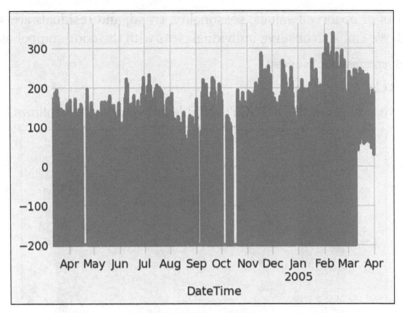

Figure 6.5: *The trend plot*

The trend plot shows a consistent plot between **April 2004 and September 2005** and shows an increasing trend from **October 2004** to **March 2005**. The **seasonality** of the data can be explained as follows:

```
seasonality = decomposed.seasonal
```

```
seasonality.plot();
```

The **seasonal** object is used to find the **seasonality of the time series data**.

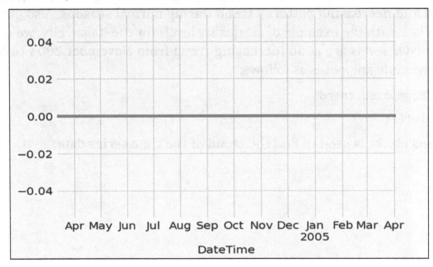

Figure 6.6: *The seasonality plot*

There is **no seasonality** in the time series data. The **residual** of the time series data can be found using the code snippet:

```
residual = decomposed.resid
residual.plot();
```

The **resid** object is used to find the **residual of the time series data**.

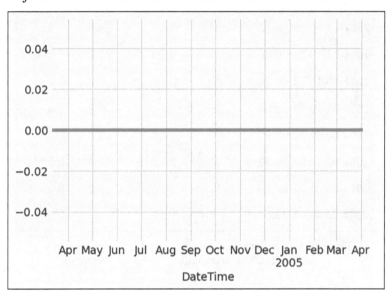

Figure 6.7: *The residual plot*

For the residuals, there are random changes in the time series data, and there are no changes in the time series data as can be seen. We can concatenate all of the above four components of **observed values, trend, seasonality**, and **residuals** into a data frame.

```
component = pd.concat([level, trend, seasonality, residual],axis=1)
component.head(10)
```

The **concat function** is used to combine all **four components** and the top 10 entries of the data frame are shown in *Figure 6.8*.

Date Time	NO2(GT)	trend	seasonal	resid
2004-03-10 18:00:00	113.0	113.0	0.0	0.0
2004-03-10 19:00:00	92.0	92.0	0.0	0.0
2004-03-10 20:00:00	114.0	114.0	0.0	0.0
2004-03-10 21:00:00	122.0	122.0	0.0	0.0
2004-03-10 22:00:00	116.0	116.0	0.0	0.0
2004-03-10 23:00:00	96.0	96.0	0.0	0.0
2004-03-11 00:00:00	77.0	77.0	0.0	0.0
2004-03-11 01:00:00	76.0	76.0	0.0	0.0
2004-03-11 02:00:00	60.0	60.0	0.0	0.0
2004-03-11 03:00:00	-200.0	-200.0	0.0	0.0

Figure 6.8: *The combined data frame with the components of observed values, seasonality, trend, and residual*

The observations are the three components of **trend, seasonality,** and **residuals**. There are top 10 rows in the concatenated data and there is no seasonality at the beginning of the data but if we explore more, there may be seasonality in the data.

All the four components were shown graphically. The seasonality of the time series data can help improve the **accuracy of the forecast models and make more accurate forecasts**.

Autocorrelation and Partial Autocorrelation

Autocorrelation and partial autocorrelation are the two tools by which we can identify patterns in the time series data. It helps identify the patterns and dependencies in the data.

Autocorrelation

Autocorrelation is the statistical relationship that gives the correlation of the time series data with its own lagged values. It measures how much the current value is deviated from the previous value.

For instance, there are time series of daily rainfall measurements (in centimeters let's say), and the autocorrelation of today's level is related to yesterday's level, the day before yesterday's level, and so on. If the **autocorrelation is high**, then the consecutive days must have had similar levels of rainfall.

The code snippet is given as follows:

```
# Autocorrelation of NO2 level
plot_acf(df["NO2(GT)"],lags=20,title="NO2")
plt.show()
```

The **plot_acf()** function is used and **20 lags** are used.

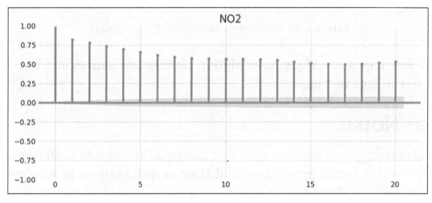

Figure 6.9: *The autocorrelation function*

The correlation results show that the **first few lags have high and positive correlation values and are statistically significant** since it cross the shaded line meaning the **NO2 level remains the same over a few hours**. The correlation values keep decreasing from the **zeroth lag to the 5th lag and stay consistent**.

Partial Autocorrelation

Partial Autocorrelation is the measure of the correlation between the observations of a time series that are **separated by k time units after adjusting for the presence of other short terms of shorter lag**.

In partial autocorrelation, the direct relation is calculated between the lag and the observation value. The code snippet is as follows:

```
# Partial Autocorrelation of NO2 level
plot_pacf(df["NO2(GT)"],lags=20)
plt.show()
```

The `plot_pacf()` function is used with a **lag of 20**.

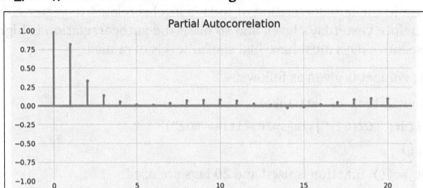

Figure 6.10: *The partial autocorrelation function*

The **first few lags and values have higher correlation values** and **decrease as the number of lags increases**.

White Noise

White noise is a type of random signal that has **equal amplitude at all frequencies**. It is often used in **signal processing and time series analysis as a reference or baseline signal**. In Python, you can generate and visualize white noise using various libraries, such as **NumPy** and **Matplotlib**. The code snippet is as follows:

```python
import numpy as np
import matplotlib.pyplot as plt


# Define the sample rate and the duration
sample_rate = 1000
duration = 1.0


# Generate a time array
t = np.arange(int(sample_rate * duration)) / sample_rate


# Generate white noise
noise = np.random.normal(0, 1, len(t))
```

```
# Plot the white noise
plt.plot(t, noise)
plt.xlabel('Time')
plt.ylabel('Amplitude')
plt.title('White Noise')
plt.show()
```

This code generates a **time array t** using the **arange function** to represent the **time axis**. Then, it generates white noise using the `random.normal` function from NumPy, which generates **random numbers following a Gaussian distribution with mean 0 and standard deviation 1**. Finally, it plots the white noise using Matplotlib's plot function.

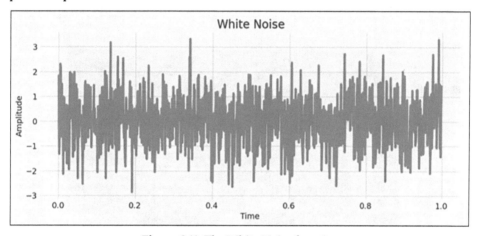

Figure 6.11: *The White Noise function*

The resulting plot shows a **random signal with equal amplitude at all frequencies**, representing white noise. Since the amplitude is generated from the **random normal function**, a different pattern is always generated.

The white noise is **naturally random in nature** and doesn't have any specific patterns or trends. It is commonly used as a **reference signal for comparison or as a source of randomness in simulations and experiments**.

Visualizing Time Series Data

The data frame can be represented using the heatmap as shown here. However, we also showed in the previous sections visually representing **seasonality, trend,** and **residuals for the NO2 levels**. From the heatmap, we can extract the correlation between other entities for Air Quality measurements. The code snippet is as follows:

```
f, ax = plt.subplots(figsize = (12,10))
sns.heatmap(df.corr(),
            annot = True,
            linecolor = 'r',
            linewidths = .5,
            fmt = '.1f',
            ax = ax);
```

The preceding code uses the **Seaborn library** and the `heatmap()` function to represent the data frame. The line color is red, the annotations parameter is set to True.

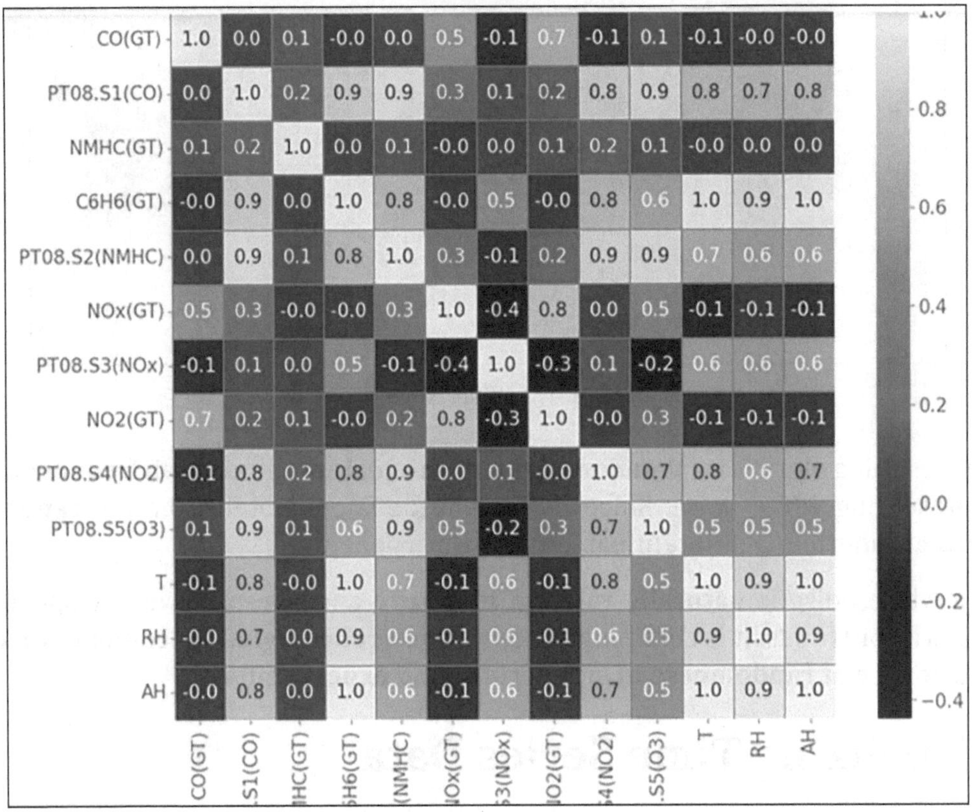

Figure 6.12: The heatmap of the data frame

There are high correlation values of **0.9 and 0.8** in some cases. For example, **PT08. S2 (NMHC)** is highly positively correlated to **PT08.S1 (CO)** with a **correlation**

coefficient of 0.9. The variable of C6H6(GT) is highly positively correlated to **PT08.S1 (CO)** with a **correlation coefficient of 0.9**. The variable of **NOx(GT)** is **highly positively correlated to NO2(GT)** with a **correlation coefficient of 0.8**.

Time Series Forecasting

Time Series Forecasting is the prediction of results about various kinds of datasets, for example, **sales forecasting for a particular company, and stock price prediction.** This will help the investors understand how the company is performing in the stock market and then make intelligent decisions, weather prediction to forecast any natural calamity in the near future and so on. We will look into various forecasting models and apply them to understand how they perform on the example dataset. Some of the time series forecasting models are **Simple Moving Average (SMA), Exponential Smoothing, Auto Regressive, Moving Average, ARMA, ARIMA, and some deep learning models** too.

Simple moving average

Simple Moving Average (SMA) is the time series forecasting model that uses the **average over a set of data points from a time series over a set of time periods**. Here, a window of points is taken that are shifted from the original set of data points. It is called the **moving average** because **new data points come up** making the **older points disappear** and not being used for the calculation. It is the most fundamental of forecasting algorithms available and does help in revealing underlying trends in the data.

In the following code snippet, we will explore the **SMA model** and also visualize the forecasted value.

```
train_size = int(len(df) * 0.7)

train_set, test_set = df[:train_size], df[train_size:]

#Simple Moving Average

#https://www.kaggle.com/code/gauravduttakiit/timeseries-forecasting
-with-simple-moving-average

y_observed_sma = df["NO2(GT)"].copy()

ma_window = 3

y_observed_sma['sma_forecast'] = df["NO2(GT)"].rolling(ma_window).mean()

y_observed_sma['sma_forecast'][train_size:] = y_observed_sma['sma_
forecast'][train_size-1]

plt.figure(figsize=(20,5))
```

```
plt.grid()
plt.plot(train_set['NO2(GT)'], label='Train')
plt.plot(test_set['NO2(GT)'], label='Test')
plt.plot(y_observed_sma['sma_forecast'], label='Simple moving average
forecast')
plt.legend(loc='best')
plt.title('Simple Moving Average Method')
plt.show()
```

The preceding code uses the **train and test datasets** that are divided based on the **70:30 format**. The **train data is 70% of the data** and the **test data is 30% of the data**. The **rolling()** function is used and a **window size of 3 days is used** meaning the last 3 days' observation for each point in the time series. The window size parameter can be changed accordingly and we can observe the changes depending on our requirement. A **smaller window size** will keep up with the **data very closely and can also pick up noise**, on the contrary, a **larger window size will not follow the data** closely, and have a **more generic smooth line**.

The **train**, **test**, and **forecasted data** are visualized using the **matplotlib** function.

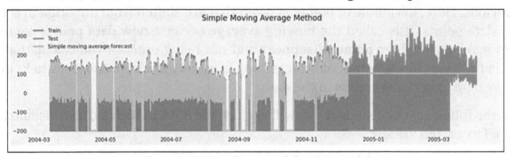

Figure 6.13: *Visualization of the SMA model*

The **blue line is the train data**, the **orange line is the test data** and the **yellow line is the Simple moving average forecasted model**.

Exponential Smoothing

Exponential Smoothing is the time series forecasting model that calculates the weighted average of the past data points, and the weights decrease exponentially with the older data points. The latest observations are given more importance than the older ones.

There are different types of exponential smoothing methods, such as **Simple**

Exponential Smoothing, Double Exponential Smoothing (also known as Holt's method), and Triple Exponential Smoothing (also known as Holt-Winters' method).

We will look into the following code to understand the implementation of the Exponential Smoothing time series model.

```python
from statsmodels.tsa.api import SimpleExpSmoothing
```

```python
#https://analyticsindiamag.com/hands-on-guide-to-time-series-analysis-
using-simple-exponential-smoothing-in-python/
```

```python
#First Model
```

```python
model1 = SimpleExpSmoothing(df['NO2(GT)']).fit(smoothing_level=0.2,
optimized=False)
```

```python
model_fit1 = model1.forecast(3).rename('alpha=0.2')
```

```python
#Second Model
```

```python
model2 = SimpleExpSmoothing(df['NO2(GT)']).fit(smoothing_level=0.8,
optimized=False)
```

```python
model_fit2 = model2.forecast(3).rename('alpha=0.8')
```

```python
#Third Model
```

```python
model3 = SimpleExpSmoothing(df['NO2(GT)']).fit()
```

```python
model_fit3 = model3.forecast(3).rename('alpha=%s'%model3.model.
params['smoothing_level'])
```

```python
#After creating the models we visualize the plots
```

```python
ax = df['NO2(GT)'].plot(marker='o', color='black', figsize=(12,8),
 legend=True)
```

```python
#Plot for alpha =0.2
```

```python
model_fit1.plot(marker='+', ax=ax, color='red', legend=True)
```

```python
model1.fittedvalues.plot(marker='+', ax=ax, color='blue')
```

```python
#Plot for alpha = 0.8
```

```python
model_fit2.plot(marker='o', ax=ax, color='blue', legend=True)
```

```python
model2.fittedvalues.plot(marker='o', ax=ax, color='red')
```

```
#Plot for alpha=Optimized by the statsmodel
model_fit3.plot(marker='*', ax=ax, color='green', legend=True)
model3.fittedvalues.plot(marker='*', ax=ax, color='green')
plt.show()
```

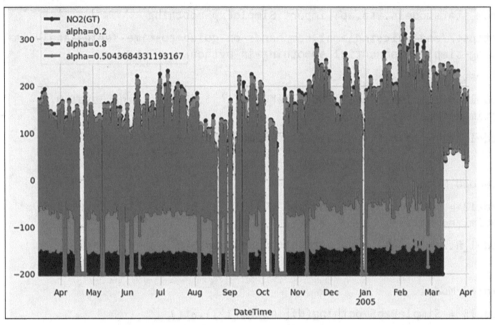

Figure 6.14: *Visualization of the Exponential Smoothing model along with forecasts with alpha values*

We are using the Exponential Smoothing model by changing the **alpha parameter (0.2, 0.8, and the optimized model). A value close to 0 means past observations have higher weights** and a **value close to 1 means current observations have higher weights**, that is, **current observations influence the forecasts**. There are three models and visualizations. We are using the `SimpleExpSmoothing` function, the `smoothing_level` **is 0.2**, and the **steps are three**. The **Smoothing level is changed to 0.8 and the optimized value of 0.50.**

Autoregressive (AR)

Autoregressive (AR) models are used for modeling and forecasting time series data. An AR model of **order n, (AR(n))** is a time series model that uses the previous time stamp data points as input to a regression equation to predict the next step.

In an `AR(n) model`, the forecasted variable is a linear function of the **previous n data points**. For example, an AR(1) model would be:

```
Yt = α + β*Y(t-1) + εt
```

Here, `Yt` is the output at the time stamp **t**, **α** is the constant, **β** is the coefficient of the previous value `Y(t-1)`, and **εt** is the error.

The following code snippet demonstrates the **AR (1) model** with **order = (1,0,0)**.

```
from statsmodels.tsa.arima.model import ARIMA
# Fit the AR model (let›s assume we›re fitting an AR(1) model)
model = ARIMA(df[‹NO2(GT)›], order=(1, 0, 0))
model_fit = model.fit()
# Make a forecast
forecast = model_fit.forecast(steps=5)
print(‹Forecast: ‹, forecast)
```

Output:

```
Forecast:  2005-04-04 15:00:00    147.587421
2005-04-04 16:00:00     131.166890
2005-04-04 17:00:00     117.760660
2005-04-04 18:00:00     106.815399
2005-04-04 19:00:00      97.879349
Freq: H, Name: predicted_mean, dtype: float64
```

The **ARIMA model** is imported from the **statsmodels library**. ARIMA (Autoregressive Integrated Moving Average) model and the **forecast()** method is used here. The forecasting is done for the **next 5 time stamps**.

If we observe the model using the **model_fit.summary()** method, we get the results as follows:

SARIMAX Results

Dep. Variable:	NO2(GT)	**No. Observations:**	9357
Model:	ARIMA(1, 0, 0)	**Log Likelihood**	-53459.778
Date:	Sun, 24 Sep 2023	**AIC**	106925.555
Time:	12:01:20	**BIC**	106946.987
Sample:	03-10-2004	**HQIC**	106932.834
	- 04-04-2005		
Covariance Type:	opg		

	coef	std err	z	P>|z|	[0.025	0.975]
const	58.1359	8.426	6.900	0.000	41.622	74.650
ar.L1	0.8164	0.011	73.742	0.000	0.795	0.838
sigma2	5371.0784	77.770	69.063	0.000	5218.651	5523.506

Ljung-Box (L1) (Q):	680.10	**Jarque-Bera (JB):**	29184.65
Prob(Q):	0.00	**Prob(JB):**	0.00
Heteroskedasticity (H):	1.13	**Skew:**	-0.95
Prob(H) (two-sided):	0.00	**Kurtosis:**	11.44

Figure 6.15: *The summary of the Autoregressive Model*

The model summary has a **P-value of 0 which is < 0.05** signifying that the NO2 level **variable is stationary.**

ARIMA

ARIMA (Autoregressive Integrated Moving Average) is a time series forecasting model that has three components, namely, **Autoregressive (AR)** refers to the current observation which is calculated based on the previous data points, **Integrated (I)** is the number of nonseasonal differences needed to make the time series stationary, and **Moving Average (MA)** gives the linear combination of the errors of the previous lags.

The ARIMA models are used as `ARIMA(p,d,q)` where 'p' is the order of the AR term, 'd' is the number of differencing to make the time series stationary, and 'q' is the order of the MA term.

We will understand how to select the values of **p**, **d**, and **q** and make an ARIMA model by using the parameters. Since the data is already stationary, we will not be doing the ADF test again. We will do the **Autocorrelation and Partial Autocorrelation** of the data to find the value of **q and p** respectively. To find the value of d, we use the differencing technique. The code for this is as follows:

```
plt.rcParams.update({‹figure.figsize›:(9,7), ‹figure.dpi›:120})
```

```
# Original Series
#https://analyticsindiamag.com/quick-way-to-find-p-d-and-q-values-for-arima/
fig, (ax1, ax2, ax3) = plt.subplots(3)
ax1.plot(df[‹NO2(GT)›]); ax1.set_title(‹Original Series›); ax1.axes.
xaxis.set_visible(False)
# 1st Differencing
ax2.plot(df[‹NO2(GT)›].diff()); ax2.set_title(‹1st Order Differencing›);
ax2.axes.xaxis.set_visible(False)
# 2nd Differencing
ax3.plot(df[‹NO2(GT)›].diff().diff()); ax3.set_title(‹2nd Order Differencing›)
plt.show()
```

The **original NO2 level variable is plotted** along with the **first-order differencing** and the **second-order differencing**. The main objective is to identify the optimal value of **d** for which the differencing level has less noise. The plots for the preceding code are as follows.

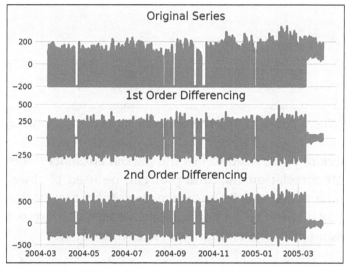

Figure 6.16: *The differencing plots for the NO2 level variable to find d*

From the preceding plots, we can observe that both the first and second-order difference plots look very similar, thus we cannot be completely sure, whether to take 1 or 2, but let's **fix d** as **1st order differencing** and then we can iterate with 2 also later.

The autocorrelation plot is also used to check the differencing value on the original plot.

```
from statsmodels.graphics.tsaplots import plot_acf
fig, (ax1, ax2, ax3) = plt.subplots(3)
plot_acf(df[‹NO2(GT)›], ax=ax1)
plot_acf(df[‹NO2(GT)›].diff().dropna(), ax=ax2)
plot_acf(df[‹NO2(GT)›].diff().diff().dropna(), ax=ax3)
```

The **plot_acf()** function is used to do the **first order differencing and the second order differencing**.

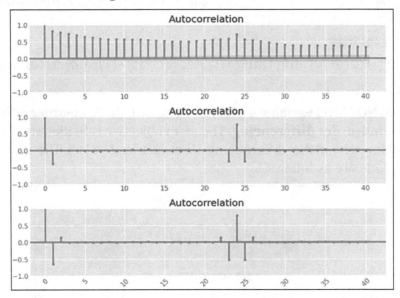

Figure 6.17: *The ACF plots for first-order differencing and second-order differencing*

To **find the value of p**, we need to use the **partial autocorrelation (PACF) plot**. The **partial autocorrelation function plot** can be used to draw a correlation between the time series and its lag while the other intermediate lags can be ignored. This plotting will let us know about the lags that are not necessary in the autoregression part. The code snippet is as follows:

https://analyticsindiamag.com/quick-way-to-find-p-d-and-q-values-for-arima/

```
from statsmodels.graphics.tsaplots import plot_pacf
plot_pacf(df[‹NO2(GT)›].diff().dropna())
```

The **plot_pacf()** function is used to perform the partial autocorrelation function.

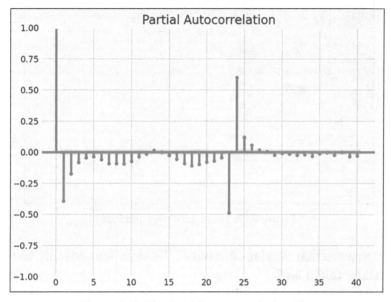

Figure 6.18: *The Partial Autocorrelation Plot*

We can take the **value of p as 1** since the second lag performs better than the first lag and is within the limit too. Although, if we look closely the fifth lag performs better than all the first four lags, so **we can also consider p as 4**.

To find the value of q, we need to use the **Autocorrelation (ACF) plot**. It helps us to understand the amount of moving average needed to remove the autocorrelation from the stationary series. The code is as follows:

```
plot_acf(df[‹NO2(GT)›].diff().dropna())
```

The **plot_acf()** function is used to perform the ACF plot operation on the NO2 level variable. The ACF plot is as follows:

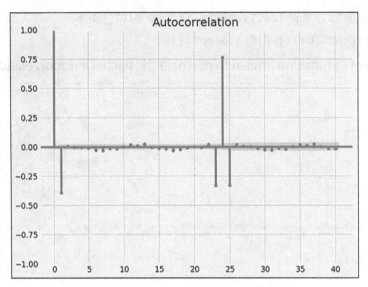

Figure 6.19: The Autocorrelation Plot

Here we can observe that two lags are out of the significance limit, so the **optimal value of q can be taken as** 2.

Next, we build the ARIMA model using the **p = 1, d = 1, and q = 2** values.

```
# Fit the AR model (let›s assume we›re fitting an AR(1) model)
model = ARIMA(df[‹NO2(GT)›], order=(1, 1, 2))
model_fit = model.fit()
# Make a forecast
forecast = model_fit.forecast(steps=5)
print(‹Forecast: ‹, forecast)
```

Output:

```
Forecast:  2005-04-04 15:00:00      156.726490
2005-04-04 16:00:00      152.392795
2005-04-04 17:00:00      148.767562
2005-04-04 18:00:00      145.734973
2005-04-04 19:00:00      143.198144
Freq: H, Name: predicted_mean, dtype: float64
```

The model is created for the next five steps. Next, we observe the summary of the model using the **.smodel_fitummary() function.**

```
model_fit.summary()
```

```
SARIMAX Results
```

Dep. Variable:	NO2(GT)	No. Observations:	9357
Model:	ARIMA(1, 1, 2)	Log Likelihood	-52756.665
Date:	Sun, 24 Sep 2023	AIC	105521.329
Time:	18:16:42	BIC	105549.905
Sample:	03-10-2004	HQIC	105531.034
	- 04-04-2005		
Covariance Type:	opg		

	coef	std err	z	P>|z|	[0.025	0.975]
ar.L1	0.8365	0.015	54.101	0.000	0.806	0.867
ma.L1	-1.3401	0.018	-73.473	0.000	-1.376	-1.304
ma.L2	0.3652	0.015	24.210	0.000	0.336	0.395
sigma2	4626.8545	29.347	157.661	0.000	4569.336	4684.373

Ljung-Box (L1) (Q):	2.44	Jarque-Bera (JB):	57442.17
Prob(Q):	0.12	Prob(JB):	0.00
Heteroskedasticity (H):	1.09	Skew:	-2.37
Prob(H) (two-sided):	0.01	Kurtosis:	14.18

Figure 6.20: *The model summary*

The **p-value is still 0** and the AIC value is reduced from the previous model (106925) to 105521.

We can also test with **p = 1, d = 2,** and **q = 2** values.

```
# Fit the AR model (let›s assume we›re fitting an AR(1) model)
model = ARIMA(df[‹NO2(GT)›], order=(1, 2, 2))
model_fit = model.fit()


# Make a forecast
forecast = model_fit.forecast(steps=5)


print(‹Forecast: ‹, forecast)
```

Output:

```
Forecast:  2005-04-04 15:00:00     167.111512
2005-04-04 16:00:00     167.054147
2005-04-04 17:00:00     167.054739
2005-04-04 18:00:00     167.061655
2005-04-04 19:00:00     167.069261
Freq: H, Name: predicted_mean, dtype: float64
```

The predicted values remain the same more or less the same at **167 approximately**. The model summary is as follows:

```
model_fit.summary()
```

The `model_fit.summary()` function is used to find the summary of the model and the screenshot of the model is represented as follows:

SARIMAX Results					
Dep. Variable:	NO2(GT)	**No. Observations:**	9357		
Model:	ARIMA(1, 2, 2)	**Log Likelihood**	-52917.155		
Date:	Sun, 24 Sep 2023	**AIC**	105842.309		
Time:	18:23:58	**BIC**	105870.884		
Sample:	03-10-2004	**HQIC**	105852.014		
	- 04-04-2005				
Covariance Type:	opg				

	coef	std err	z	P>|z|	[0.025	0.975]
ar.L1	0.1091	0.022	4.934	0.000	0.066	0.152
ma.L1	-1.5907	0.029	-55.372	0.000	-1.647	-1.534
ma.L2	0.5908	0.022	26.300	0.000	0.547	0.635
sigma2	4789.4983	133.372	35.911	0.000	4528.093	5050.903

Ljung-Box (L1) (Q):	0.25	**Jarque-Bera (JB):**	54386.60
Prob(Q):	0.61	**Prob(JB):**	0.00
Heteroskedasticity (H):	1.12	**Skew:**	-2.28
Prob(H) (two-sided):	0.00	**Kurtosis:**	13.89

Figure 6.21: The model summary with changed p,d, and q values

The **P-value in this model is < 0.05** which makes it **statistically significant,** and the AIC value has increased to 105842 from the previous model. **AIC** is the Akaike Information Criterion that helps explain the **strength of the linear regression model**. It explains the **goodness of the fit**. Lower AIC means the model is better than the higher AIC model.

Here is a very good article to interpret the ARIMA model parameters.

https://analyzingalpha.com/interpret-arima-results

https://www.machinelearningplus.com/time-series/arima-model-time-series-forecasting-python/

The predicted plot can be represented by the code as follows:

```
# Actual vs Fitted


from statsmodels.graphics.tsaplots import plot_predict


plot_predict(model_fit, dynamic = False)
plt.show()
```

The **plot_predict()** function is used to plot the predicted values.

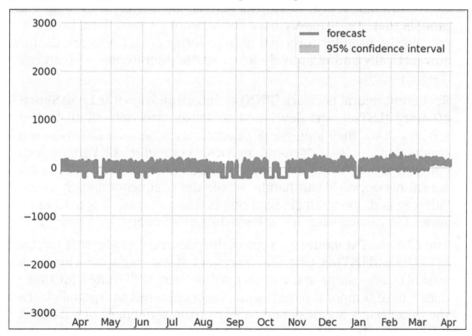

Figure 6.22: *The predicted plot using the ARIMA model*

FbProphet

FbProphet is a flexible and efficient time series forecasting algorithm based on **additive models where non-linear trends** are fit with **yearly, weekly, and daily seasonality**. It also considers holidays into consideration to perform the forecasting operation. It is based on the **Bayesian approach** which also provides room for uncertainty estimation in the predictions.

https://pypi.org/project/fbprophet/

https://medium.com/illumination/understanding-fb-prophet-a-time-series-forecasting-algorithm-c998bc52ca10#:~:text=FBProphet%20is%20a%20powerful%20time,uncertainty%20estimation%20in%20the%20predictions.

Deep Learning for Time Series Forecasting (CNN and LSTM)

Deep Learning for time series forecasting using **Convolutional Neural Networks (CNN)** and **Long Short Term Memory (LSTM)** is very useful considering the kind of data and time series forecasting problems we are solving. Here are definitions and applications of CNN and LSTM algorithms in time series forecasting.

- **Convolutional Neural Networks (CNNs)** are the **class of deep learning models** that are primarily used for analyzing visual data, however, they can also be used for forecasting time series data. CNNs are designed to automatically and adaptively learn spatial hierarchies of features from the input data.

- **Recurrent neural network (RNN)** architecture known as **Long Short-Term Memory (LSTM)** was developed to better precisely simulate temporal sequences and their long-range dependencies. Because LSTM has feedback connections, it is a "general purpose computer" (it can perform any computation a Turing machine can) in contrast to standard feedforward neural networks. It can handle whole data sequences, such as audio or video, in addition to single data points (like pictures). It is perfect for time series forecasting since it can keep data in "memory" for a long time.

- The **CNN-LSTM model** is a type of deep learning model that has the **best of CNNs and LSTMs**. CNNs are excellent at learning spatial hierarchies or spatial relationships in the data, making them well-suited for time series data where temporal patterns can be considered as "spatial". LSTMs, on the other hand, are designed to learn from sequences of data by storing information from past data points, making them ideal for time series forecasting.

Evaluation of Time Series Forecasting Models

Evaluating time series forecasting models is an important step in the model-building process. It helps understand the **model's performance and accuracy** in making future predictions. The evaluation process typically involves training a set of models on a training set and assessing its accuracy on the unseen test set. There are several metrics, including **Mean Absolute Percentage Error (MAPE), Mean Error (ME), Mean Absolute Error (MAE), Mean Percentage Error (MPE), Root MEAN Squared Error (RMSE), Lag 1 Autocorrelation of Error (ACF1), Correlation between the Actual and the Forecast (corr), Min-Max Error (minmax)** that are used to evaluate the performance of time series forecasting models.

Exploring the Parameters in the Time Series Models

The time series models are statistical tools for temporal data analysis and forecasting. These models are based on the idea that the data points represent the realization of a series of random variables, indicating the existence of an underlying stochastic process.

When there are various parameters involved in the time series models, we need to explore the relevant points with respect to the models and the data. Among them, some of them are as follows:

- **Trend:** A Trend is defined as a consistent **upward or downward movement** in a time series. Trends can be **probabilistic or deterministic** and identifying trends in the data helps to **uncover hidden patterns in the data for long-term analysis and forecasting**.

- **Seasonality:** Seasonality primarily points to seasonal changes in the data temporally. In this case, we can identify the buying patterns of customers, or rising and falling of stock prices during certain situations of the year, or climatic changes that affect various places in the world.

- **Correlation between attributes:** There are situations when the time series variables are correlated.

The **ARIMA (Autoregressive Integrated Moving Average)** model has the parameters of **p (order of autoregression), d (degree of differencing), and q (order of moving average)** that are changed iteratively and we can make better models.

In the case of deep learning models like **CNN (Convolutional Neural Networks) and LSTM (Long Short-Term Memory)**, parameters such as **the number of layers, the number of neurons in each layer, the type of activation function, and the learning rate** are among the important factors to consider.

The process of parameter selection is fundamentally iterative. There may be some initial value of parameters that we start with and then iteratively change to improve the model performance with time.

Performance Metrics of the Models to Measure their Accuracy

In the context of time series forecasting, many performance metrics are used to **evaluate the accuracy of the models**. These metrics compare the **forecasted values with the observed values** and give a quantitative measure of the quality of the forecasts. We will discuss MAPE, MAE, MSE, and RMSE as follows:

- **Mean Absolute Percentage Error (MAPE):** MAPE is the measure of the prediction accuracy of a forecasting model. It expresses accuracy as a percentage and is defined by the formula **MAPE = mean(abs((observed value- forecast value) /observed value)) * 100%**. The lower the MAPE, the better the model's performance.

- **Mean Error (ME):** ME is the average of the forecast errors, where the **forecast error is the difference between the observed value and the forecasted value** divided by the total number of samples. A **positive ME** indicates that the **forecasted values are lower than the actual values**, while a **negative ME** indicates that the **forecasted values are higher than the actual values**. A ME close to zero suggests that the forecasts are unbiased.

- **Mean Absolute Error (MAE):** Without taking into account their direction, MAE calculates the average magnitude of the differences in a group of projections. All individual variances are given **equal weight in the test sample's average** of the **absolute difference between the forecasted value and the observed value**.

- **Mean Squared Error (MSE):** MSE is the square of the difference between the forecasted value and the observed value. It is used frequently along with **MAE and RMSE**. It depends on the forecast model and the problem at hand on which performance metrics we will be using.

- **Root Mean Squared Error (RMSE):** RMSE is a frequently used measure of the differences between values predicted by a model and the values observed. It is the **square root of the average of squared differences between forecasted and actual observations** over a defined time period.

$$RMSE = sqrt(mean((actual-forecasted)^2))$$

- **Lag 1 Autocorrelation of Error (ACF1)**: ACF1 measures the correlation between a value and the preceding (lagged by 1-time unit) value. In this context, it measures the correlation between an error and the error at the next time point.

These metrics have different requirements as far as the accuracy and the performance of the forecasting are concerned. We mostly use **MAE, MSE, RMSE, ACF1,** and so on, but we also use other performance metrics **as per the need of the problem and the forecasting model**.

Auto Time Series Libraries

The Auto time series libraries are the tools that help automate the process of time series forecasting. They perform operations like **data preparation, feature engineering, model selection, and forecasting**. Since these tools already cover all the mentioned operations in quick and organized succession with minimum human intervention, they help save a lot of time and also develop accurate time series models. This way there are **avenues for better prediction over the traditional time series forecasting libraries**.

One of the libraries that was already discussed is the **fbprophet** in which the algorithm is based on **additive models where non-linear trends** are fit with **yearly, weekly, and daily seasonality**. It also considers holidays into consideration to perform the forecasting operation. There are also a few other libraries, we will look into **atspy, auto-ts, statsforecast, pmdarima, ts-automl, tsfresh, sktime, Arch time series financial library, and pyflux**.

Atsypy is an automated time series model using Python. It has various automated time series models as in the following screenshot:

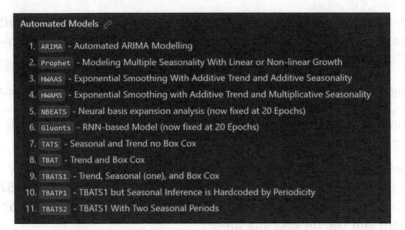

Figure 6.23: *The automated models provided by Atspy*

https://github.com/firmai/atspy

- **Auto_TS** is a library that automates the process of **building multiple time series models using a single line of code**. It supports models like **ARIMA, Seasonal ARIMA, Prophet, and scikit-learn machine learning algorithms**. It also has **Dask** to handle millions of rows.

  https://github.com/AutoViML/Auto_TS

- **Statsforecast** library provides **fast and accurate implementations of AutoARIMA, AutoETS, AutoCES, MSTL, and Theta models in Python**. These models exploit autocorrelations in the time series data. **Here** is a very good blog on the usage of Statsforecast (https://towardsdatascience. com/fast-time-series-forecasting-with-statsforecast-694d1670a2f3).

  https://github.com/Nixtla/statsforecast

- **Pmdarima** library is a **Python wrapper for the R package "forecast"** and **provides auto ARIMA functionality**. It automatically selects the **best ARIMA model for a given time series**. Here is also a very good article to explain of the usage of pmdarima.

  https://github.com/alkaline-ml/pmdarima

  https://towardsdatascience.com/efficient-time-series-using-pythons-pmdarima-library-f6825407b7f0

- **Ts-automl** is a library that provides automated **time series forecasting using machine learning models**. It offers different pipeline classes for different types of models, such as slow, fast, and balanced.

  https://github.com/MMurilloGlez/ts-automl

- **Tsfresh** is a library for **automated feature extraction and selection for time series data**. It **automatically extracts a large number of features from time series** and **selects the most relevant ones for modeling**.

https://github.com/blue-yonder/tsfresh

- **Sktime** provides a **unified interface for multiple time series learning tasks**. Currently, this includes **time series classification, regression, clustering, annotation, and forecasting**. It comes with time series algorithms and scikit-learn compatible tools to **build, tune, and validate time series models**.

  https://github.com/sktime/sktime

- **Arch** is a time series financial library that helps in financial stock price forecasting, and financial econometrics. It is abbreviated as **Autoregressive Conditional Heteroskedasticity (ARCH)** and is written in Python (with Cython and/or Numba used to improve performance).

  https://github.com/bashtage/arch

- **PyFlux** is an open-source time series Python library that has a **good array of modern time series models**, as well as a **flexible array of inference options (frequentist and Bayesian)** that can be applied to these models.

  https://github.com/RJT1990/pyflux

These are the few automated time series forecasting models that **help save time and resources** and **improve the workflow of time series forecasting models**. It also helps in **augmenting the accuracy of the prediction models**.

Conclusion

This chapter covered the necessities of time series analysis and forecasting, the properties of time series data, including **seasonality, trends, stationarity, white noise, the different types of time series data, and the visualization of the time series data**. These properties of the data when explored give us deeper insights on the data that cannot be done by straightforward data analysis. We have taken a real-life dataset from the UC Irvine data repository to **analyze the time series data of the air quality of an Italian city**. On that, we have tested algorithms, such as **AR, MA, ARMA, ARIMA, Exponential Smoothing, Fbprophet, and CNN-LSTM**. All the codes are in Python and we have also discussed the **tuning of the relevant parameters**, such as **trend, seasonality, and so on**. We also learned about some important performance metrics of time series forecasting models, including **MAE, MSE, RMSE, MAPE**, and so on. Additionally, we have also learned about some very interesting and **efficient automated time series libraries** that not only **save us a lot of time and resources but also make the models accurate**. In the next chapter, we will do **data analysis of voice and audio data** using Python libraries.

References

- White Noise

https://medium.com/@ms_somanna/guide-to-adding-noise-to-your-data-using-python-and-numpy-c8be815df524

Keywords

Time Series Forecasting, Seasonality, Trend, Visualization, AR, ARMA, ARIMA, Exponential Smoothing, Autocorrelation, Partial Autocorrelation, Stationarity, Auto time series libraries

CHAPTER 7

Signal Processing

Introduction

Python is widely used in data analysis and can also be used for audio signal analysis. We take a closer look at signal processing with Python in this chapter.

This thorough book will provide you with an in-depth understanding of audio signals, their various representations, and the methods used to manipulate them. It will also cover transformers for audio data, transcription, voice recognition, and text-to-speech analysis using the `HuggingFace` package and Python.

The essential ideas of time and frequency domain representations—which serve as the fundamentals of audio signal analysis—will be our main emphasis. Additionally, we will understand how to see these signals in both domains. The Fourier Transform, a crucial mathematical tool for navigating between the various domains of time and frequency, will also be covered in this chapter.

Upon completion of this chapter, the readers will be able to deal with audio signals and create their application be it text-to-speech or automatic speech recognition or transcription.

Structure

In this chapter, we will discuss the following topics:

- Introduction to Signal Processing
  - Brief Overview of Signal Processing and its Importance in Data Analysis
  - Introduction to Audio Signal Processing and its Applications

- Understanding Audio Data
  - o Basics of Audio Data: sampling rate, amplitude, bit depth, waveform, and spectrograms
  - o Introduction to Python Libraries for Audio Data Processing
- Audio Signal Processing Techniques
  - o Introduction to Various Audio Signal Processing Techniques
  - o Use of Python for Implementing these Techniques
- Speech Recognition and Transcription
  - o Techniques used in Speech Recognition and Transcription
  - o Walkthrough of a Python Code Example for Speech Recognition and Transcription

Introduction to Signal Processing

Signal Processing is an important branch of engineering that deals with the **analysis, interpretation, and manipulation of signals**. Signals, in this context, can be anything that carries information, such as **audio, voice, images, or even financial stock market data**. The field is divided into **analog signal processing and digital signal processing**, with the latter being heavily in use due to the rise of cheap hardware and digital technologies. The primary goal of signal processing is to extract useful information from this kind of data and convert it into a format that is easier to interpret. This discipline finds extensive applications in various fields, **including telecommunications, image processing, seismology, and even in the medical field for processing ECG, EEG, and MRI data**.

Brief Overview of Signal Processing and its Importance in Data Analysis

Signal Processing is a fundamental discipline in the fields of data science, engineering, and various other fields that deal with the extraction, analysis, and manipulation of signals. A signal is any information be it audio, video, temperature data, stock market data, and so on, that changes over time or space.

Signal processing is crucial to data analysis because it allows us to derive **actionable insights from unstructured data** and **apply those insights to decision-making**. It serves as the foundation for a wide range of technologies that we use daily, including **computers, radios, cell phones, and smart devices**.

In the context of time-series data, signal processing is used to **analyze patterns and trends to predict future values based** on historical data points. This is particularly important in various industries, such as **finance and weather forecasting**, where accurate predictions can lead to **significant cost savings and efficiency improvements**.

Signal processing also involves various **preprocessing and filtering techniques to improve the quality of the data for analysis**. Techniques such as **moving averages, rolling windows, and different types of filters (low-pass, high-pass, and band-pass)** are used to **smooth time-series data and reduce the impact of noise**.

Moreover, studying signals in the **frequency and time domains depends on auditory signal processing**. Analyzing signals and data points about time is known as **time-domain analysis**. On the other hand, **frequency domain analysis** looks at how signals behave about frequency. Significant patterns and features in the data that are not immediately visible in the raw data can be found through these studies.

The applications of **signal processing are diverse and span several fields**. For instance, in the **Internet of Things (IoT), signal processing** is used to **extract valuable information from sensor data, leading to actionable insights**. In healthcare and biomedical applications, various signal processing techniques help detect different abnormalities in the patient's body, assess and diagnose the patient's health conditions, and plan the treatment accordingly. There are also fields like environmental monitoring, weather forecasting, and industrial automation, where the data is captured by sensors and then analysis is carried out.

As the digital world continues to expand, signal processing faces new challenges and opportunities. The ever-growing data source from various devices and platforms can lead signal processing to reinvent itself, in **connection with techniques from distributed computing, optimization, or machine learning**.

In conclusion, signal processing is a crucial discipline that plays a pivotal role in data analysis. Providing the tools and techniques to extract meaningful information from raw data, enables us to make sense of the world around us and make informed decisions.

https://www.datacamp.com/tutorial/a-data-scientists-guide-to-signal-processing

https://theconversation.com/signal-processing-a-field-at-the-heart-of-science-and-everyday-life-89267

https://signalprocessingsociety.org/our-story/signal-processing-101

Introduction to Audio Signal processing and its Applications

Audio signal processing, also known as audio processing, is the **method of interpreting and manipulating auditory signals to alter the way they sound** or to extract information from them. It can be performed in **either the time or frequency domain and can be applied to both analog and digital signals**.

With the introduction of the telephone, phonograph, and radio in the early 20th century, audio signals could now be sent and stored. This marked the beginning of the history of audio signal processing. The mid-1900s saw Bell Laboratories play a major role in the development of signal processing theory and its audio application. The field's early contributions to **communication theory, sampling theory, and pulse-code modulation (PCM)** by pioneers like **Claude Shannon and Harry Nyquist** served as its cornerstones.

An **analog audio signal is a continuous signal** that is equivalent to **airborne sound waves in terms of electrical voltage or current**. The next step in analog signal processing is to **physically modify the continuous signal using electrical circuits to adjust its voltage,** current, or charge. Historically, the only way to modify a signal was through analog before the widespread use of digital technology.

Since the development of digital technology, many applications **now prefer to use digital signal processing**. However, because analog technology frequently yields nonlinear answers that are **challenging to duplicate with digital filters**, it is frequently still preferred in music applications.

Audio signal processing has a wide range of applications. These can be put as audio data storage, audio data processing, data compression, music information retrieval, automatic speech recognition, text-to-speech processing, acoustic detection, and noise cancellation, to name a few.

Automatic Speech recognition (ASR) is another vital application of audio signal processing. It helps **extract information from the speech signals and then translates it into recognizable words**. Speech recognition technology is found in many applications, from "talk to text" applications on smartphones to recognition programs for people with disabilities.

To conclude, audio signal processing is a comprehensive field with diverse applications ranging from music and entertainment to telecommunications and health care. As technology continues to evolve, the importance and influence of audio signal processing are likely to increase further.

https://signalprocessingsociety.org/our-story/signal-processing-101

https://www.coursera.org/lecture/audio-signal-processing/introduction-to-audio-signal-processing-fHha1

https://www.ee.iitb.ac.in/student/~daplab/publications/chapter9-prao.pdf

Understanding Audio Data

Sound signals are studied and manipulated in the intriguing and intricate field of audio data. It is essential to many applications, including **voice recognition, audio streaming, and even medical diagnostics**. Let's examine the fundamentals of audio data and how it is represented digitally so that you can completely understand the idea.

Since audio transmissions are analog, they are **continuous in both amplitude and time**. Real-world sounds are created by waves traveling across a medium, such as the air. **Microphones** pick up these waves and translate them into an electrical signal. The frequency and amplitude of the original sound wave are precisely reflected in this signal.

To convert this **analog signal into a digital format, sampling is used**. Sampling involves measuring the **amplitude of the signal at regular intervals, known as the sampling rate**. A common **sampling rate for audio is 44.1 kHz**, which means the **signal is measured 44,100 times per second**. Each of these measurements is **known as a sample.**

After sampling, the digital audio data is usually **stored in a file format like WAV or MP3**. These formats include not only the actual audio data, but also **metadata such as the number of channels (mono or stereo), the sample rate, and the bit depth**. The **bit depth** refers to the **number of bits that are used to represent each sample**. A **higher bit depth allows for a more precise representation of the audio signal** but also results in larger file sizes.

Understanding audio data also involves understanding **how to manipulate and process it**. For example, audio data can be filtered to remove certain frequencies, or it can be amplified to increase the volume. These operations are typically performed using **digital signal processing (DSP)** techniques.

Finally, it's important to note that audio data can be analyzed and interpreted in various ways. For instance, a **spectrogram** can be used to **visualize the frequency content of an audio signal over time**. Machine learning algorithms can also be applied to audio data for tasks such as **speech recognition or music genre classification**.

To sum up, deciphering audio data comprises of variety of steps, including **recording sound waves, transforming them into a digital format, processing and modifying them, and interpreting the outcomes**. It's an intriguing area with many uses, ranging from entertainment to medical.

https://towardsdatascience.com/understanding-audio-data-fourier-transform-fft-spectrogram-and-speech-recognition-a4072d228520

Audio Data

Several concepts of audio data help us understand the data and derive decisions from them: **sampling rate, amplitude, bit depth, waveform,** and **spectrograms**. Let's explore each of these to understand the basics of audio data.

- **Sampling Rate**

The **sampling rate**, often **measured in kilohertz (kHz)**, is the number of audio samples recorded per second. Each sample represents the amplitude of the audio at a particular moment in time. The higher the sample rate, the more accurately the audio can be represented, resulting in a higher resolution.

The **Nyquist-Shannon sampling theorem** states that to accurately reconstruct any signal of a required bandwidth, the **sampling frequency must be greater than twice the highest frequency of the signal being sampled**. If lower sampling rates are used, the original signal's information may not be completely recoverable from the sampled signal.

- **Amplitude and Bit Depth**

Amplitude in digital audio is often expressed in **decibels (dB)**. It defines the magnitude of the sound wave, which we understand as volume normally. The higher the amplitude, the louder the sound.

Bit depth refers to the **number of bits used to represent each sample of audio**. In digital audio, a bit is a **binary unit of information that can have a value of either 0 or 1**. The bit depth determines the **number of possible amplitude values that can be assigned to each sample**. The higher the bit depth, the greater the resolution and dynamic range of the audio.

- **Waveform**

Waveforms are graphical representations of audio signals. In the context of audio, they represent how the **amplitude of a sound signal changes over time**. They can be used to identify **loud sections, quiet sections, and silence in an audio clip.**

- **Spectrograms**

A spectrogram is a visual representation of the **spectrum of frequencies in a sound or other signal as they vary with time**. This map of frequencies helps to identify the areas that can be manipulated and played with to understand the audio and recreate new audio. Spectrograms are used extensively in the **field of signal processing and are a useful tool for musicologists**, as they can identify **different sounds, and their changes and interactions, visually over time**.

In conclusion, understanding these basic components of audio data is crucial for anyone involved in digital audio production, whether it's **music creation, podcasting, or audio** for **video production**. It allows you to make informed decisions about the **audio quality, file size, and processing power** needed for your specific project.

https://www.lalal.ai/blog/sample-rate-bit-depth-explained/

https://legacy.presonus.com/learn/technical-articles/Sample-Rate-and-Bit-Depth

https://huggingface.co/learn/audio-course/chapter1/audio_data

Introduction to Python Libraries for Audio Data Processing

Audio processing in Python involves manipulating, analyzing, and understanding audio signals. Several libraries are available in Python to conduct audio data processing, each with its strengths and use cases. We will be mainly using the `Librosa` library to load the data and explain the concepts of amplitude, frequency, time domains, spectrograms, waveforms, and sampling rates.

`Librosa` is the Python package for **music and audio analysis**.

https://librosa.org/

We will be referring to the HuggingFace Audio Course to create the codes, do the visualizations, and explain the concepts. There are also some other packages like PyAudio, pydub, pyAudioAnalysis, pyAudioProcessing, TorchAudio, Essentia, and SoundFile to name a few.

https://huggingface.co/learn/audio-course/chapter1/audio_data

https://pypi.org/project/PyAudio/

https://github.com/jiaaro/pydub

https://github.com/tyiannak/pyAudioAnalysis

https://github.com/jsingh811/pyAudioProcessing

https://github.com/pytorch/audio

https://github.com/MTG/essentia

https://github.com/bastibe/python-soundfile

The introductory codes are as follows. We import the **librosa** library and then load the **trumpet** sound from the dataset and visualize it. The **matplotlib** library is used to visualize the data.

```
import librosa
array, sampling_rate = librosa.load(librosa.ex("trumpet"))
import matplotlib.pyplot as plt
import librosa.display
plt.figure().set_figwidth(12)
librosa.display.waveshow(array, sr=sampling_rate)
```

The data is visualized in the time domain. The **waveshow function** from **librosa** is used to represent the waveform.

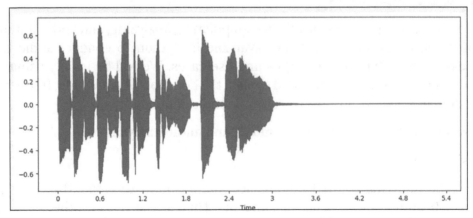

Figure 7.1: *The time domain data representation of the trumpet audio*

The preceding graph has the **amplitude on the y-axis** and **time on the x-axis**. The sampling rate is **22050 Hz or 22.5 KHz** and each point in time is the single sample value that was obtained when the signal was sampled.

We can also look into the **array variable** that is a numpy array.

```
array[:5]
array([-1.4068246e-03, -4.4607770e-04, -4.1098156e-04,  9.9922603e-05,
        4.3147978e-05], dtype=float32)
```

For the frequency domain representation, we will be using the **Discrete Fourier Transform (DFT)** to convert the time domain signal to the frequency domain signal. Here, we will be using the **rfft()** function from **numpy** library. We will look into **8192 samples** from the sound data and then use the window function to identify the frequency components present in the signal.

```
import numpy as np
dft_input = array[:8192]
# calculate the DFT
window = np.hanning(len(dft_input))
windowed_input = dft_input * window
dft = np.fft.rfft(windowed_input)
```

The **dft** variable is an array of complex numbers consisting of real and imaginary components.

```
print(dft)
[-2.18180002e-04+0.00000000e+00j -2.04155426e-05-1.08952556e-03j
  9.24083484e-04+1.93526629e-04j ... -8.31871101e-08+3.38487353e-06j
 -3.02099704e-06-3.69307347e-06j  3.64474469e-06+0.00000000e+00j]
```

We will look into the individual real and imaginary components of the **dft** variable.

```
# get the amplitude spectrum in decibels
amplitude = np.abs(dft)
amplitude_db = librosa.amplitude_to_db(amplitude, ref=np.max)
amplitude_db
array([-80., -80., -80., ..., -80., -80., -80.])
```

The **abs()** function from **numpy** is used to find each component's absolute values (amplitude) in the **dft** variable. The **librosa.amplitude_to_db()** is used to **convert the amplitude values to the decibel scale**.

```
# get the frequency bins
frequency = librosa.fft_frequencies(sr=sampling_rate, n_fft=len(dft_in-
put))
#Visualizing the frequency domain
plt.figure().set_figwidth(12)
plt.plot(frequency, amplitude_db)
plt.xlabel("Frequency (Hz)")
plt.ylabel("Amplitude (dB)")
plt.xscale("log")
```

The `librosa.fft_frequencies()` is used to get the frequency bins meaning the **sampling rate and the length of the sound signal** are used to have each component that will be used to represent the frequencies. The plot of the frequency domain representation is shown as follows:

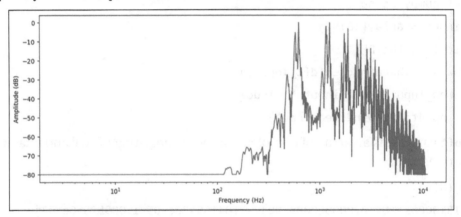

Figure 7.2: *The frequency domain data representation of the trumpet audio data*

The preceding plot represents the **strength of the various frequency components** that are present in **the audio file of length 8192 samples**. The **frequency values are on the x-axis**, and their **amplitudes are on the y-axis**.

The frequency values are represented by the **frequency** variable.

```
frequency
array([0.00000000e+00, 2.69165039e+00, 5.38330078e+00, ...,
       1.10196167e+04, 1.10223083e+04, 1.10250000e+04])
```

We will be observing **Spectrogram** using the **librosa** library. It plots the **frequency, amplitude, and time representation** of the audio signal. Short-Time Fourier Transform (STFT) is used to take multiple DFTs where only a small section of time is used, and then the resulting spectra are stacked together into a spectrogram.

```
#Spectrogram
D = librosa.stft(array)
S_db = librosa.amplitude_to_db(np.abs(D), ref=np.max)
plt.figure().set_figwidth(12)
librosa.display.specshow(S_db, x_axis="time", y_axis="hz")
plt.colorbar()
```

The **specshow()** function is used to represent the spectrogram. The **decibel scale** is created using the **amplitude_to_db()** function. The Spectrogram is represented as follows:

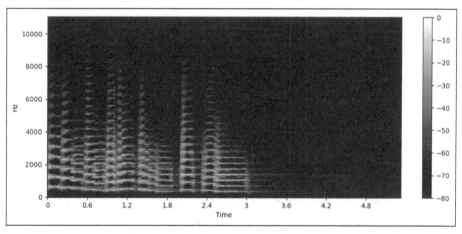

Figure 7.3: *The Spectrogram representation of the trumpet audio data*

In the preceding plot, the **x-axis represents time**, and the **y-axis represents frequency in Hz**. The **intensity of the color gives the amplitude or power of the frequency** component at each point in time, measured in decibels (dB).

The spectrogram is created by **taking short segments of the audio signal**, typically lasting a few milliseconds, and calculating the **discrete Fourier transform** of each segment to obtain its frequency spectrum. The **resulting spectra are then stacked together on the time axis to create the spectrogram**. Each **vertical slice in this image corresponds to a single frequency spectrum**, seen from the top. By default, **librosa.stft()** splits the **audio signal into segments of 2048 samples**, which gives a good trade-off between frequency resolution and time resolution.

Next, we will be looking into **Mel Spectrogram**. It is similar to Spectrogram but has the frequency represented in a non-linear scale. This way the visualization will be easier to understand concerning the hearing as perceived by a human. The human auditory system is **more sensitive to changes in lower frequencies than higher frequencies**, and this **sensitivity decreases logarithmically as frequency increases**.

To create the `mel spectrogram`, the STFT is used just like creating the Spectrogram, that is splitting the audio into short sections to obtain a sequence of frequency spectra. Then, each spectrum is sent through a set of filters called the **mel filterbank**, to **transform the frequencies to the mel scale**.

```
#Mel Spectrogram

S = librosa.feature.melspectrogram(y=array, sr=sampling_rate,
n_mels=128, fmax=8000)

S_dB = librosa.power_to_db(S, ref=np.max)

plt.figure().set_figwidth(12)

librosa.display.specshow(S_dB, x_axis="time", y_axis="mel", sr=sampling_
rate, fmax=8000)

plt.colorbar()
```

In the preceding code the parameter `n_mels` is the **number of mel bands to generate**. The mel bands are a **set of frequency ranges that divide the spectrum into perceptually meaningful components**, using a set of filters whose shape and spacing are chosen to mimic the way the human ear responds to different frequencies. Common values for **n_mels are 40 or 80**. fmax indicates the **highest frequency (in Hz) we care about**.

Just as the regular spectrogram, the mel spectrogram has the amplitude, time, and frequency represented. The amplitude is commonly referred to as a **log-mel spectrogram**, because the **conversion to decibels involves a logarithmic operation**. The preceding example used `librosa.power_to_db()` as `librosa.feature.melspectrogram()` creates a power spectrogram.

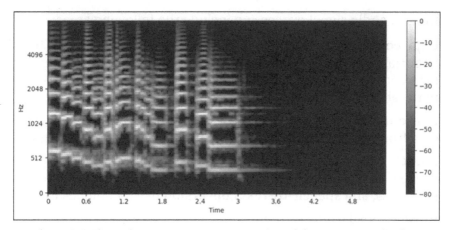

Figure 7.4: *The Mel spectrogram representation of the trumpet audio data*

Compared to the normal spectrogram, the Mel spectrogram can **capture more meaningful features of the audio signal for human perception**, making it a popular choice in tasks such as **speech recognition, speaker identification, and music genre classification**.

Audio Signal Processing Techniques

The electronic manipulation of audio signals is the primary importance of audio signal processing, also sometimes referred to as **audio processing**. These signals are **longitudinal waves made up of compressions and rarefactions** that propagate through the atmosphere as electronic representations of sound waves. Analog or digital formats can be used to describe audio signals, and either domain can be used for processing. Digital processors use mathematics to process the digital representation of an electrical signal, whereas analog processors deal directly with the signal.

Introduction to Various Audio Signal Processing Techniques

Techniques for processing audio signals have a long history; they were essential to the **invention of the telephone and phonograph as well as early radio broadcasts**. Significant advancements in digital audio coding and audio data compression have been accomplished over time. These advancements include **modified discrete cosine transform coding, adaptive DPCM, differential pulse-code modulation, and linear predictive coding**.

Applications of audio signal processing include the following areas:

- **Data compression and storage:** Since audio signals can be big, it's important to store them effectively. By using methods, such as audio data compression, the size of the audio files can be decreased without noticeably lowering their quality,

- **Music information retrieval:** This is the process of obtaining relevant data from music files, such as the **genre, tempo, mood, or pitch**,

- **Speech processing:** This is the process of interpreting and analyzing spoken language. Applications such as **voice recognition, speech synthesis, and speech-to-text conversion** use techniques in this field,

- **Noise Cancellation:** To reduce unwanted noise and enhance the quality of the audio signal, this technique creates an "anti-noise" signal,

- **Audio synthesis:** Audio synthesis is the process of creating audio signals through electronics. A synthesizer is a type of **musical instrument that carries out this function**. Synthesizers can produce **original sounds or mimic existing ones**.

- **Audio Effects:** These modify the sound of an audio source, such as a musical instrument. **Distortion, filters, modulation, pitch, time, and dynamic effects** like volume pedals and compressors are examples of common effects.

The discipline of audio signal processing has also made use of deep learning techniques. These methods have been applied to **tracking, localization, ambient sound detection, music information retrieval, and speech recognition**. Additionally, they have been applied to the synthesis and manipulation of audio, including source separation and audio enhancement.

The processing of audio signals is a vital part of our everyday existence. Audio signal processing methods enable and improve the efficiency of our interactions with our smart gadgets, including the music we listen to, phone calls we make, and voice instructions we give them.

https://www.ee.iitb.ac.in/student/~daplab/publications/chapter9-prao.pdf

https://arxiv.org/abs/1905.00078

https://towardsdatascience.com/audio-deep-learning-made-simple-part-1-state-of-the-art-techniques-da1d3dff2504

https://www.wiley.com/en-us/Digital+Audio+Signal+Processing%2C+3rd+Edition-p-9781119832676

Use of Python for Implementing these Techniques

We have used the technique of **fast Fourier transform (FFT)** previously to represent the signal in the frequency domain. We can also use MFCC to represent the signal. **Mel Frequency Cepstral Coefficients (MFCC)** are a few characteristics, typically between 10 and 20, that characterize a spectral envelope's general form. MFCCs are an **effective feature for automatic speech recognition** because they may be utilized to represent the "speech envelope."

Here's a detailed explanation of how MFCCs are computed:

1. **Framing of the signal:** The first step in computing MFCCs is to **divide the continuous audio signal into short frames (typically 20-40ms long)**. This assumes that the frequencies in a signal are stationary, that is, they don't change over time.

2. **Applying the Fourier Transform:** For each frame, the Fourier Transform is applied to **convert the signal from the time domain to the frequency domain**. This results in a spectrum that **shows the intensity of each frequency in the frame**.

3. **Applying the Mel filterbank:** The spectrum is then **passed through a set of filters** called the **Mel filterbank**. The **Mel scale is a perceptual scale of pitches that approximates the human ear's response** to different frequencies. Each **filter in the filter bank is a triangular bandpass filter*** that passes frequencies within a certain range and attenuates frequencies outside this range**. The result is a set of spectral coefficients that represent the power in each Mel frequency band.

4. **Taking the logarithm:** The logarithm of **each spectral coefficient is then taken**. This step is based on the **observation that human perception of sound intensity is logarithmic.**

5. **Apply the Discrete Cosine Transform (DCT):** Finally, the **DCT is applied to the log spectral coefficients to yield the MFCCs**. The **DCT is a linear transformation that is used to de-correlate the log spectral coefficients and reduce their dimensionality**. The result is a set of MFCCs that represent the shape of the power spectrum in a compact form.

A **band-pass filter** is a device or process that **allows signals within a specific frequency range to pass through while attenuating (not permitting) signals at frequencies outside this range**. In the context of audio signal processing, a

band-pass filter is used to isolate a particular range of frequencies from an audio signal.

The **Mel filter bank is a series of band-pass filters** used in the estimation of Mel Frequency Cepstral Coefficients (MFCC). Every filter in the **Mel filterbank is a triangle band-pass filter**, which attenuates frequencies outside of its passband while passing frequencies within it. The **filters are uniformly spaced along the Mel scale**, a pitch perception scale that simulates how the human ear reacts to various frequencies. A **collection of spectral coefficients that express the power in every Mel frequency band is the result.**

We will observe the coding implementation of MFCC using the **Librosa** library.

```
#Mel Frequency Cepstral Coefficients (MFCC)


import librosa


y, sr = librosa.load(librosa.ex("trumpet"))
# Compute MFCC
mfcc = librosa.feature.mfcc(y=y, sr=sr, n_mfcc=13)


# Print shape of MFCC matrix
print(mfcc.shape)
Output:
(13,230)
```

We first load the "trumpet" sound from the previous code using **librosa.load()**. This gives the variables **y (audio time series) and sr (sampling rate)**. We then compute **mfcc** using the **librosa.feature.mfcc()** function. This takes **audio time series (y), sampling rate (sr), and number of mfcc (n_mfcc)** as the input parameters. The **mfcc.shape** gives the shape of the MFCC matrix that is, 13 rows and 230 columns.

Next, we visualize it in the form of a spectrogram.

```
import librosa.display
import matplotlib.pyplot as plt


plt.figure(figsize=(10, 4))
librosa.display.specshow(mfcc, x_axis='time')
```

```
plt.colorbar()
plt.title('MFCC')
plt.tight_layout()
plt.show()
```

The MFCC is displayed using the `librosa.display.specshow()` function. This function creates a **spectrogram where the x-axis represents time** and the **y-axis represents the different MFCCs**. The **color at each point represents the amplitude of a particular MFCC** at a particular time.

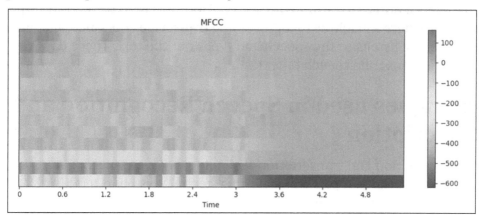

Figure 7.5: *The MFCC spectrogram representation of the trumpet audio data*

The **x-axis** is the time variable where each **column in the image represents a different time frame** in the audio signal. The audio signal is **divided into short frames (typically 20-40ms long)**, and the **MFCCs are computed for each frame**.

The **y-axis is the different MFCCs**. Each row of the image is an individual MFCC. There are a total of 13 MFCCs that we have calculated in the preceding code.

For the colors, each color at each point in the image represents a specific amplitude at a particular time. The color scale is a legend at the side of the spectrogram. **Darker colors represent lower amplitudes**, and **brighter colors represent higher amplitudes**.

https://en.wikipedia.org/wiki/Mel-frequency_cepstrum#:~:text=Mel%2Dfrequency%20cepstral%20coefficients%20(MFCCs,%2Da%2Dspectrum%22).

https://wiki.aalto.fi/display/ITSP/Cepstrum+and+MFCC

https://www.analyticsvidhya.com/blog/2021/06/mfcc-technique-for-speech-recognition/

Speech Recognition and Transcription

Speech recognition, also known as **automatic speech recognition (ASR)**, is a technology that converts speech into written text. It's an interdisciplinary field that includes electrical engineering, computer science, and languages. Numerous industries can benefit from this technology, including **healthcare, automated customer service, voice assistants like Siri and Alexa**, and transcribing services.

When it comes to speech recognition, **transcription** is the act of **turning the audible speech into written or printed text**. There are two types of transcription: **automated, where a machine recognizes and transcribes the voice**, and manual, where a person listens to the speech and types out the text. These days various AI tools also transcribe speech to text.

Techniques used in Speech Recognition and Transcription

Speech recognition and transcription technologies have evolved. Early systems were based on simple **pattern-matching** techniques, but modern systems use more **sophisticated machine-learning algorithms**. Here are some key techniques used in speech recognition and transcription:

- **Acoustic Modeling**

Acoustic modeling is the task of creating statistical representations for each distinct sound in a language. The most common approach to acoustic modeling involves **Hidden Markov Models (HMMs)**, which use statistical methods to **represent different states of speech** and the **transitions between them**.

- **Language Modeling**

Forecasting the likelihood of a word sequence is known as language modeling. This is crucial for speech recognition since it helps the system in distinguishing between word sequences that share similar sounds. For language modeling, **n-gram models and, more recently, neural network-based models** are frequently utilized.

- **Feature Extraction**

The process of converting the **unprocessed audio signal into a collection of features** that capture the **essence of the speech is known as feature extraction**. In speech recognition, **Mel Frequency Cepstral Coefficients (MFCC)** is a frequently utilized characteristic. It offers a condensed depiction of the sound's spectral envelope, which helps differentiate between phonemes or discrete units of sound.

- **Deep Learning**

Speech recognition algorithms now work better than before due to the usage of deep learning. Because they can **handle sequential data**, **recurrent neural networks (RNNs), particularly Long Short-Term Memory (LSTM) networks**, are commonly used. The most recent **transformer models**, which take **advantage of self-attention mechanisms**, have **demonstrated encouraging outcomes more recently**.

- **End-to-End Models**

End-to-end models, such as the **Listen, Attend and Spell (LAS) model**, help simplify the **speech recognition pipeline by directly transcribing the audio data into text**. These models **eliminate the need for separate acoustic and language models**, making the system simpler and potentially more accurate.

In conclusion, with developments in deep learning and machine learning, the field of speech recognition and transcription is developing faster than ever. These innovations could completely change the way we communicate with machines and handle a lot of spoken data.

Walkthrough of a Python Code Example for Speech Recognition and Transcription

The coding implementation for **speech recognition and transcription** is as follows. We will create the speech recognition and transcription models using the `Huggingface` **Transformers library.**

We'll use the **automatic-speech-recognition pipeline** to transcribe an audio recording of a person asking a question about paying a bill using the same **MINDS-14 dataset** that is used from the **datasets library**.

https://huggingface.co/learn/audio-course/chapter2/asr_pipeline

The dataset looks like this in the datasets section of the `Huggingface` website.

Figure 7.6: *The MINDS-14 dataset section as shown on the Huggingface website*

Let's start with the following code, but before that please make sure to install the transformers library. It is better to create a separate environment using **conda or pip** to **avoid any dependency issues later with the system python environment**.

https://it.engineering.oregonstate.edu/sites/it.engineering.oregonstate.edu/files/pages/virtualenv/files/python-guide.pdf

https://www.geeksforgeeks.org/python-virtual-environment/

```
!pip install –upgrade transformers
```

```
from datasets import load_dataset
from transformers import pipeline
cls = pipeline("automatic-speech-recognition")
minds = load_dataset("PolyAI/minds14", name="en-AU", split="train")
minds
Output:
Dataset({
    features: ['path', 'audio', 'transcription', 'english_
transcription', 'intent_class', 'lang_id'],
    num_rows: 654
})
```

The `minds` variable is a **dictionary datasets file** with **654 entries**. We can then use any of the entries and explore them. The **variable cls** is the automatic speech recognition model that is created using the **pipeline object** imported from the **transformers** library.

```
example = minds[500]
```

```
cls(example["audio"]["array"])
```

Output:

```
{'text': 'WHAT ONOTHEN I VILENT'}
```

The variable example is the **501st entry in the minds variable** we defined earlier.

If we do the transcription of the **example variable**, we get this.

```
example["english_transcription"]
```

Output:

```
'yes I recognize the payment'
```

The transcription result is very different from the one we got earlier and is not very clear from what we got **after cls() was passed to the data**.

We can try this for the **German split of the MINDS-14**. We will load the "de-DE" subset.

```
from datasets import load_dataset
from datasets import Audio
minds = load_dataset("PolyAI/minds14", name="de-DE", split="train")
minds = minds.cast_column("audio", Audio(sampling_rate=16_000))
example = minds[500]
example["transcription"]
```

Output:

```
ich habe bitte eine Frage ich würde gerne eine Rechnung bezahlen wie
kann ich das bitte machen
```

Let's create the automatic speech recognition pipeline like before.

```
from transformers import pipeline
cls = pipeline("automatic-speech-recognition", model="maxidl/wav-
2vec2-large-xlsr-german")
cls(example["audio"]["array"])
```

Output:

{'text': 'ruscott ich habe bitte eine frage ich würde gern eine rechnung bezahlen wie kann nich das bitte machen'}

The data is already present with us from the **MINDS dataset** and we can create the ASR model using the `pipeline()` **function**. The readymade model `maxidl/wav2vec2-large-xlsr-german` is used.

Conclusion

In this chapter, we embarked on an exploration of **audio signal processing**, delving **into the intricacies of understanding audio data, the parameters that define it, and the techniques used to process it**. We also ventured into the realm of **automatic speech recognition and transcription**, discussing their underlying principles and their practical implementation in Python.

We began by demystifying audio data, discussing its **digital representation and the various parameters that characterize it, such as sample rate, bit depth, amplitude, spectrogram, mel spectrogram, and channels**. Understanding these parameters is crucial, as they directly **impact the quality and the type of information, we can extract from the audio data**.

Next, we delved into the core techniques used in audio signal processing. We explored the **Fourier Transform, a mathematical tool that allows us to examine the frequency components of a signal**, and the **Mel Frequency Cepstral Coefficients (MFCC), a feature that provides a compact representation of the spectral envelope of a sound**. We have utilized Python code examples for each technique, **demonstrating how libraries, including 'numpy', 'scipy', 'matplotlib', and 'librosa'** can be leveraged to implement these techniques and visualize their results.

The last section of the chapter was attributed to building **automatic speech recognition and transcription pipeline** using the transformers library and also leveraged the **MINDS-14 dataset**. We discussed the fundamental techniques used in these fields, including **acoustic modeling, language modeling, feature extraction, and the use of deep learning models**. We also provided **Python code to build an end-to-end automatic speech recognition tool**, showcasing the practical application of these techniques.

In the next chapter, we will solve real-life problems by using real data. We will perform data analysis, statistical data analysis, data preparation, and data cleaning techniques to prepare the data for further modeling. We will also use some AI tools to perform data analysis to keep updated with the recent tools, trends and of course improve efficiency and performance.

CHAPTER 8

Analyzing Real-World Data Sets using Python

Introduction

Python has become the industry leader in data analysis because of its readability, adaptability, and large library of available modules for data manipulation and analysis. The goal of this chapter, *"Real-World Projects Using Python"* is to walk you through the **useful uses of Python in the analysis of real-world data sets**, emphasizing how **Python can be used to glean insightful information from complex data**.

Python's data analysis capabilities are extensive and varied, ranging from **healthcare records and environmental data to social media analytics and e-commerce trends**. We'll go into real-world examples that show how Python may be used to analyze massive volumes of data, spot trends, and make predictions.

We will explore the application of Python libraries such as **Pandas, NumPy, Matplotlib, Seaborn, scikit-learn, and SciPy** in real-world data analysis projects. These libraries provide data manipulation, analysis, and visualization functionalities, making Python a powerful tool for data science.

In this chapter, we will also introduce an **AI tool named Julius.ai**, which can be used alongside Python for data analysis. Julius provides **advanced analytical capabilities** to enhance data analysis tasks. Combining Python's robust libraries and Julius's AI-driven insights will be a powerful tool for any data analyst. Moreover, we will also look into **no-code and low-code tools, including Mito, Draw Data, PyGWalker, PivotTableJs**, and so on, to work with data analysis projects.

Structure

In this chapter, we will discuss the following topics:

- An Overview: Using Python to Analyze Real World Projects
- Understanding Real-World Data Sets
  - Characteristics of Real-World Data Sets
  - Handling Complexities in Real-world Data Sets
- Exploratory Data Analysis and Visualization using Python
- Introduction to Julius
  - Overview of Julius as an AI Tool
- Exploratory Data Analysis and Visualization using Julius
- Data Analysis Using No-code or Low-code Tools

An Overview: Using Python to Analyze Real World Projects

To close the gap between theoretical knowledge and real-world data analysis scenarios, this chapter, *"Real-World Projects Using Python,"* aims to **provide practical Python applications**. The goal is to give readers **a thorough understanding of how Python and Julius, an AI tool**, may work to make the job of data analysts smoother and more efficient.

Python, which is well-known for being straightforward and effective, is extensively used in many different fields, including **scientific computing, web development, and data analytics in particular**. Python's adaptability has made it possible for businesses in a variety of sectors, including **finance, healthcare, and digital behemoths like Google and Facebook**, to **evaluate enormous datasets and derive valuable insights**.

The chapter will demonstrate how to approach real-world datasets, which are **often messy, incomplete, and large in scale**. It will guide readers through the **end-to-end process of data analysis, from data acquisition and cleaning** to **exploratory analysis, statistical inference, and the creation of predictive models**. The focus will be on applying these methods to datasets that readers are likely to encounter in their professional lives.

Beyond Python, the chapter introduces Julius, an AI tool that **enhances data analysis and visualization processes**. The purpose here is to show how **Julius can integrate with Python to offer a more streamlined and powerful data analysis experience**. Readers will learn how Julius can **assist in automating tasks, providing AI-driven insights, and creating advanced visualizations**.

The end goal of this chapter is not only to provide knowledge but also to inspire confidence in the **reader's ability to handle real-life data**. Through practical examples and hands-on projects, **readers will learn to apply Python and Julius to make data-driven decisions**. This chapter serves as the culmination of the concepts discussed in previous chapters, focusing on application rather than theory.

By the end of the chapter, readers should be able to undertake their own data analysis projects with competence. They will have a **clear understanding of how to apply Python in real-world situations and how to leverage the capabilities of Julius to enhance their data analysis and visualization efforts**. This chapter is essential for anyone looking to apply their Python skills to real-world data and make an impact in their field.

Understanding Real-World Data Sets

Real-world datasets, often known as "raw" data, are sets of **unprocessed data points that are directly gathered from a variety of sources**. When correctly handled and inspected, these unmodified and unanalyzed datasets can yield a wealth of information. Effective data analysis begins with an **understanding of real-world datasets, particularly in Python**, which is well-known for its capacity to handle and analyze such data.

Unlike neatly packaged sample datasets used for educational purposes, **real-world datasets often come with complexities and challenges** that reflect the realities of data collection and handling in the actual world. They can be large, **containing millions or even billions of data points, and are often messy and unstructured**. They can contain **missing, inconsistent, or incorrect data**, **making them difficult to understand and analyze** without thorough cleaning and preprocessing.

Real-world datasets can be derived from various sources such as **social media feeds, machine logs, business transaction records, healthcare records, database websites like the World Bank, and the United Nations, government portals, and sensor data in IoT devices**. They can also come in various formats including **text, images, audio, video, and more**. The type of data and its **format largely depend on the data source** and the specific application for which the data is being collected.

Real-world datasets are valuable because they can yield insights that can be applied to real-world situations. We may find **patterns, trends, correlations, and anomalies by examining these databases, and these findings can help decision-makers in a variety of disciplines, including environmental science, business, and finance**.

In conclusion, knowledge of **real-world datasets is an essential competency** for data scientists and analysts. These datasets, despite their difficulties and complexities, include a multitude of data that, when properly utilized, can **yield insightful information and support well-informed decision-making in a range of real-world scenarios.**

Characteristics of Real-World Data Sets

Real-world datasets are a rich source of information, providing a snapshot of situations, behaviors, events, and interactions as they occur naturally. They are characterized by several key features, including:

- **Heterogeneous**: Real-world datasets often contain data of various types and formats, including **numerical, categorical, text, image, audio, and more**. This diversity can provide a more comprehensive view of the phenomenon under study but also poses challenges in data handling and analysis.

- **Large-scale**: These datasets are often large, sometimes **containing millions or even billions of data points**. The sheer volume of data can **provide more statistical power for analysis** but also **requires more computational resources and efficient data processing techniques.**

- **Messy and Unstructured**: Unlike clean and structured datasets used in academic settings, **real-world datasets are often messy and unstructured**. They can contain **missing values, outliers, inconsistencies, and errors** that need to be addressed during data preprocessing.

- **Temporal and Spatial Aspects**: Real-world datasets often have temporal and spatial aspects, capturing data across time and space. This can provide valuable context for analysis but also introduces additional compl**exities, such as temporal autocorrelation and spatial dependencies.**

- **Subject to Bias:** These datasets can be subject to various forms of bias, including selection bias, measurement bias, and confounding. These biases need to be carefully **considered and addressed in the data analysis to ensure valid and reliable results**.

These characteristics present both opportunities and challenges for data analysis. Understanding these features is crucial for **effectively working with real-world datasets** and extracting meaningful and actionable insights from them.

https://www.ncbi.nlm.nih.gov/pmc/articles/PMC9636688/

Handling Complexities in Real-world Data Sets

When we perform **Exploratory Data analysis (EDA)** on real-world data sets, we need to navigate through various complexities and intricacies in the datasets. We need to do **Data Analysis and visualization** but before that **data transformation, cleaning and preparation** also need to be done to get rid of the anomalies and dirty portions of the data.

One of the first steps in managing the complications of real-world data is dealing with missing values. Missing values occur **due to data entry errors, missed information while surveying, or maybe the data was not entered by mistake**, and so on. Handling of the missing values depends on the problem we are trying to solve, for example, if the **percentage of missing values is very low (<5%), we can remove them, although again we need to reverify with the clients about the kind of analysis they want, in some cases we can replace missing values with the mean or median (for numeric values) and replace with mode (for categorical values).** There can be cases where data imputation can be done to fill up the cells with missing values. The `.isnull()` function is used to check for missing values.

There can be instances where we need to explore the datatypes of each variable in the dataset. We can easily find that numerical values are tagged as string datatypes. We can use the `dtypes()` function in the pandas library to find the datatypes of each variable and convert them to the right data type. We can use functions such as `.to_numeric()` to **convert into numeric variable** and `.to_string()` into **string variable** for datatype conversion.

Analyzing distinctive values in your data might help in your comprehension of the variability within it. For instance, you may determine how many categories are there in a column that shows categories of a particular feature **by looking up the unique values in that column**. The `nunique()` function from the Pandas package can be used in Python to determine **how many unique values are present in each column**.

Lastly, data visualization is an effective method for understanding the complexity of datasets from the actual world. **Finding patterns, trends, and outliers in your data that might not be immediately** obvious in **raw, numerical data might be aided by visualizing it**. Many tools for Python, such as **Matplotlib, Seaborn**, and **plotly** can be used to create a wide range of visually appealing and educational data visualizations.

In summary, handling the complexities in real-world datasets involves a combination of data cleaning, understanding **data types, exploring unique values, and visualizing the data**. Python, with its powerful libraries and functions, provides a comprehensive toolkit for performing these tasks effectively and efficiently.

https://ecoagi.ai/articles/exploratory-data-analysis-python-pandas

Exploratory Data Analysis and Visualization using Python

In this section, we will look into the EDA and visualization of a **World Bank dataset**. The data has **nominal GDP, GDP per capita, Population, % GDP growth for the year 2022, and %share of GDP of that country** in the world economy. We will go through the steps of Data Analysis and Visualization. The dataset was chosen from the World Bank to analyze data **that is very fresh and connected to the world**.

So, we start with the Python codes and proceed step-by-step, accordingly.

```
import pandas as pd
import numpy as np
import matplotlib.pyplot as plt
import seaborn as sns
```

We install the relevant libraries, and next, we **load the Excel file and display the first five rows of the data**.

```
# Create a DataFrame
df = pd.read_excel('GDP data.xlsx')
df.head(5)
```

The **first five rows of the data frame** are as follows. We can start exploring the data now.

```
df.head(5)
```

#	Country	GDP (nominal, 2022)	GDP	GDP (growth)	Population (2022)	GDP per capita	Share of World GDP
0	17	Saudi Arabia	1108150000000	1.108 trillion	0.0874	36408820	30436	0.0110
1	167	Comoros	1242519407	1.24 billion	0.0239	836774	1485	0.0000
2	166	Grenada	1256413185	1.26 billion	0.0580	125438	10016	0.0000
3	16	Indonesia	1319100000000	1.319 trillion	0.0531	275501339	4788	0.0131
4	15	Spain	1397510000000	1.398 trillion	0.0545	47558630	29385	0.0139

Figure 8.1: The first five rows of the dataset

The preceding data is not in any order as per the nominal GDP, GDP per capita, or Population. We will look into further analysis as we dive deeper.

```
print(df.info())
```

The main information of the data frame df is as follows:

```
<class 'pandas.core.frame.DataFrame'>
RangeIndex: 177 entries, 0 to 176
Data columns (total 8 columns):
 #   Column               Non-Null Count  Dtype
---  ------               --------------  -----
 0   #                    177 non-null    int64
 1   Country              177 non-null    object
 2   GDP (nominal, 2022)  177 non-null    int64
 3   GDP                  177 non-null    object
 4   GDP (growth)         177 non-null    float64
 5   Population (2022)    177 non-null    int64
 6   GDP per capita       177 non-null    int64
 7   Share of World GDP   177 non-null    float64
dtypes: float64(2), int64(4), object(2)
memory usage: 11.2+ KB
None
```

Figure 8.2: The information of the data frame

The dataset has 177 nations and thankfully, there are no missing values. The variable GDP and GDP (nominal, 2022) are the same, so we can remove the GDP variable from the data frame. The datatypes of each variable are also fine and need not be changed.

```
df = df.drop(['GDP'], axis=1)
```

After deleting the GDP variable, we can check the descriptive statistics of each of the numeric variables.

```
print(df.describe())
```

The `.describe()` function gives the descriptive statistics of the data frame.

```
                #  GDP (nominal, 2022)  GDP (growth)  Population (2022)  \
count  177.000000         1.770000e+02    177.000000       1.770000e+02
mean    89.000000         5.588979e+11      0.041038       4.368887e+07
std     51.239633         2.404638e+12      0.066641       1.560540e+08
min      1.000000         6.034939e+07     -0.291000       1.131200e+04
25%     45.000000         1.356313e+10      0.023900       2.388992e+06
50%     89.000000         4.575234e+10      0.039300       9.038309e+06
75%    133.000000         3.010250e+11      0.058100       3.347587e+07
max    177.000000         2.546270e+13      0.578000       1.425887e+09

       GDP per capita  Share of World GDP
count      177.000000          177.000000
mean     16825.977401            0.005554
std      23072.367011            0.023913
min        238.000000            0.000000
25%       2322.000000            0.000100
50%       6728.000000            0.000500
75%      20795.000000            0.003000
max     127046.000000            0.253200
```

Figure 8.3: *The descriptive statistics of the numerical values of the data frame*

We can extract some information from *Figure* 8.3, for example, in the nominal GDP column, **75% of the countries have less than 3 trillion US dollars of nominal GDP** and the **bottom 25%** has **less than 135 billion US dollars of nominal GDP**. We can also see that 75% of nations contribute to **0.03% share to the nominal GDP**. The maximum contribution is made by the US with a **staggering 25%**. This shows that the majority of the world's wealth is controlled by a few countries, and most of the nations are poor. Although, we can completely conclude by analyzing the GDP per capita of each nation. The GDP per capita is a direct indicator of a country's development, which is obvious if there are nations with **very high populations and low GDP per capita**. For that, we can look into bivariate analysis graphs for certain variables like GDP per capita and population.

```
sns.pairplot(df)
```

```
plt.show()
```

The preceding code helps create scatter plots between the numeric variables. We will look into some graphs that we find have a relation between variables, be it a positive or negative relation.

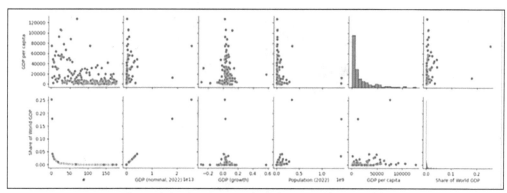

Figure 8.4: *Bivariate analysis between the variables*

The **4th graph on the first row in** *Figure* 8.4 is the **GDP per capita and Population graph**. If we look closely, then we can see that less populated nations have very high GDP per capita. **GDP per capita** is defined as the **nominal GDP divided by the country's population.** So, in this case, each individual has a lot of money on him/her which is a very good thing as far as the development of the country is concerned. If we also see there are two outliers in the plot, that have very low GDP per capita.

If we also see the plot of Share of **World GDP and Population (4th plot in the 2nd row)**, we can see that the **two nations are outliers**, that is, they have high populations as well as **more than 15% contribution to the World GDP, they are the US and China. India is there as an outlier population,** but its **share of the World GDP cannot be considered an outlier**. Probably, in a few years, we can see **India as a significant contributor to the World's nominal GDP**.

You, the readers, can do more analysis using various other variables too.

Let's do the correlation matrix heat map on the variables to get a numeric value of correlation.

```
columns_of_interest = ['GDP (nominal, 2022)', 'GDP (growth)',
'Population (2022)', 'GDP per capita', 'Share of World GDP']
```

```
corr_matrix = df[columns_of_interest].corr()
```

```
sns.heatmap(corr_matrix, annot=True)
```

```
plt.show()
```

The **df.corr()** function is used to create the correlation matrix.

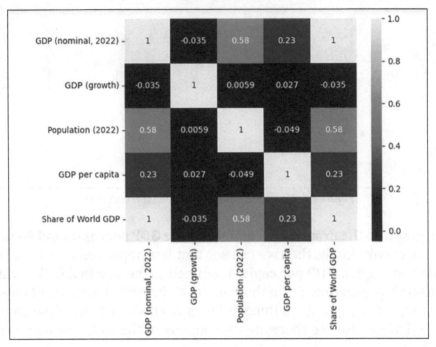

Figure 8.5: *Correlation Matrix heat map*

From the preceding heat map, there is a **maximum correlation coefficient of 0.58** between the **share of world GDP and Population** and **GDP nominal and Population**. The **GDP per capita and the Share of World GDP** have a **coefficient value of 0.23**. If we observe the negative correlation coefficients, countries with more GDP growth have less nominal GDP for obvious reasons since **larger economic nations can't grow as fast as smaller nations can**. There is always a **saturation or plateau point where the larger economic powerhouses reach and slow down their growth,** or even the economies contract, like it's happening for Japan as an example.

We can look at the top 10 countries with the highest nominal GDP.

```
# Top 10 countries by GDP
top_gdp_countries = df.sort_values(by='GDP (nominal, 2022)',
ascending=False).head(10)

plt.figure(figsize=(12, 6))

sns.barplot(x='Country', y='GDP (nominal, 2022)', data=top_gdp_countries,
palette='viridis')

plt.title('Top 10 Countries by GDP (Nominal) in 2022')

plt.ylabel('GDP (Nominal) in Billion USD')
```

```
plt.xticks(rotation=45, ha='right')
plt.show()
```

The .sort_values() function is used to have the **countries in descending order in terms of nominal GDP.** The bar graph is as follows.

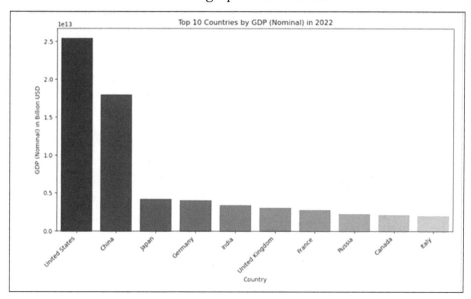

Figure 8.6: *10 Nations with the maximum nominal GDP*

The preceding bar graph has **10 countries with maximum nominal GDP.** We can easily say from this graph that these **10 countries hold the majority of the world's wealth**. This can be proved using a **pie chart to show the %share of World GDP.**

Let's check the 10 countries with the lowest nominal GDP.

```
# Bottom 10 countries by GDP
top_gdp_countries = df.sort_values(by='GDP (nominal, 2022)', ascending
=True).head(10)
plt.figure(figsize=(12, 6))
sns.barplot(x='Country', y='GDP (nominal, 2022)', data=top_gdp_countries,
palette='viridis')
plt.title('Top 10 Countries by GDP (Nominal) in 2022')
plt.ylabel('GDP (Nominal) in Billion USD')
plt.xticks(rotation=45, ha='right')
plt.show()
```

It is the same code, except in the **sort_values(), ascending is made to True**. The bar graph is as follows:

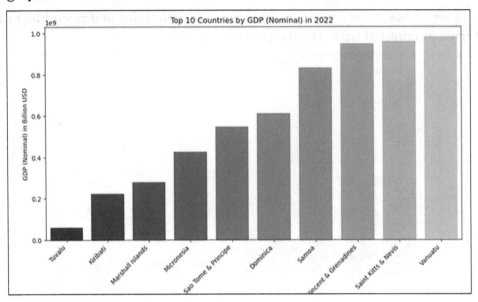

Figure 8.7: *10 Nations with the Minimum Nominal GDP*

It's an interesting concept which we can find here. The nations are all **Pacific island nations and the population is very low too**, this does not mean that all of them are poor or politically or socially disturbed nations. Since the **population is low, their production is also minimal** and they **do not trade a lot with larger nations**. Thus, they have the least nominal GDP.

We can perform some statistical data analysis on the dataset. For that, we are installing **statsmodels and the scipy** package.

```
from scipy import stats
from sklearn.linear_model import LinearRegression
from statsmodels.stats.outliers_influence import variance_inflation_factor
# Variable importance
model = LinearRegression()
model.fit(df[['Population (2022)']], df['GDP per capita'])
print('R-squared:', model.score(df[['Population (2022)']], df['GDP per capita']))
Output:
R-squared: 0.0024223163260445046
```

Here, a linear regression model is being created using the `LinearRegression` **class** from a machine learning library scikit-learn. The model will be used to **predict the dependent variable ('GDP per capita') based on the independent variable ('Population (2022)').**

The `fit()` method is called on the model, which takes the **independent variable ('Population (2022)') and the dependent variable ('GDP per capita') as arguments.** This step **trains the linear regression model on the provided data**, attempting to find the **best-fit line that minimizes the difference between the predicted and actual values of GDP per capita based on population.**

The score method is used to calculate the R-squared (coefficient of determination) of the model. **R-squared is a statistical measure** that represents the proportion of variance in the **dependent variable ('GDP per capita')** that is predictable from the **independent variable ('Population (2022)').** It is between 0 and 1, where 1 is the perfect fit.

The R-squared value is 0.0024 in this case. A **higher R-squared value generally indicates a better fit of the model to the data**. In the context of linear regression, it **represents the proportion of the variance in the GDP per capita that is explained by the population.**

We can look into Hypothesis testing with the following demo code.

```
# Hypothesis testing
alpha = 0.05
# Shapiro-Wilk normality test
shapiro_test = stats.shapiro(df['GDP per capita'])
print('Shapiro-Wilk normality test:', shapiro_test)
if shapiro_test[1] > alpha:
    print('GDP per capita follows normal distribution')
else:
    print('GDP per capita does not follow normal distribution')
```

Output:

```
Shapiro-Wilk normality test: ShapiroResult(statis-
tic=0.704981803894043, pvalue=2.031437959347131e-17)
GDP per capita does not follow normal distribution
```

The variable **alpha is set to 0.05**. This is the **significance level for the hypothesis test**. In hypothesis testing, the significance level (often denoted by alpha) is the

probability of rejecting the null hypothesis, when it is true. A common choice is 0.05, **which means there is a 5% chance of rejecting the null hypothesis when it is true.**

The **Shapiro-Wilk test for normality** is being performed on the **'GDP per capita'** **column of the DataFrame df**. This test checks whether a **given sample follows a normal distribution**. The result of the test is stored in the variable **shapiro_test**.

The result of the Shapiro-Wilk test is printed to the console. It typically consists of a test **statistic and a p-value**. In this case, the output is just the tuple **shapiro_test**, which includes these values.

The code then checks if the **p-value obtained from the Shapiro-Wilk test** (**shapiro_test[1]**) **is greater than the significance level alpha**. If the **p-value is greater than alpha**, the code prints 'GDP per capita follows the normal distribution,' indicating that there **is not enough evidence to reject the null hypothesis that the data follows a normal distribution**. If the **p-value is less than or equal to alpha**, the code prints 'GDP per capita does not follow the normal distribution,' suggesting that **there is evidence to reject the null hypothesis**.

The **p-value < alpha** which signifies that **GDP per capita does not follow the normal distribution.**

We can check the t-test too using the following code.

```
# t-test for the difference in means
t_test = stats.ttest_ind(df['GDP per capita'][df['Country'] == 'USA'],
                         df['GDP per capita'][df['Country'] == 'India'])
print('t-test:', t_test)
if t_test[1] > alpha:
    print('No significant difference in means')
else:
    print('Significant difference in means')
Output:
t-test: TtestResult(statistic=nan, pvalue=nan, df=nan)
Significant difference in means
```

The code is performing a **t-test for the difference in means between the 'GDP per capita' values for the countries 'USA' and 'India'**. The **ttest_ind function from the scipy.stats module** is used for an independent two-sample t-test.

The result of the **t-test is stored in the variable t_test**, which is a **tuple containing the test statistic and the p-value**.

The code then checks if the **p-value obtained from the t-test (t_test[1]) is greater than the significance level alpha**. If the p-value is greater than alpha, the code prints 'No significant difference in means,' suggesting that there is not enough evidence to reject the null hypothesis, indicating no difference in means between the two groups. If the p-value is less than or equal to alpha, the code prints 'Significant difference in means,' suggesting that there is evidence to reject the null hypothesis, indicating a significant difference in means between the two groups.

In this case, there is a significant difference in means.

Then we look into the **Analysis of Variance (ANOVA)** code here.

```
# ANOVA test for checking if country affects GDP per capita
anova_test = stats.f_oneway(df['GDP per capita'][df['Country'] == 'USA'],
                            df['GDP per capita'][df['Country'] == 'China'],
                            df['GDP per capita'][df['Country'] == 'India'])
print('ANOVA test:', anova_test)
if anova_test[1] > alpha:
    print('Country does not affect GDP per capita')
else:
    print('Country affects GDP per capita')
```

Output:

```
ANOVA test: F_onewayResult(statistic=nan, pvalue=nan)
Country affects GDP per capita
```

The code is performing an **Analysis of Variance (ANOVA) test to assess if the country has a significant effect on the 'GDP per capita' values**. The f_oneway function from the scipy.stats module is used for this test. In this case, the 'GDP per capita' values for three countries ('USA', 'China', and 'India') are passed as separate groups to the function.

The result of the ANOVA test is stored in the **variable anova_test**, which is a tuple containing the **test statistic and the p-value**.

The code then checks if the **p-value obtained from the ANOVA test (anova_test[1]) is greater than the significance level alpha**. If the **p-value is greater than alpha, the code prints 'Country does not affect GDP per capita,' suggesting that there is not enough evidence to reject the null hypothesis, indicating no significant difference in means between the groups. If the p-value is less than or equal to alpha, the code prints 'Country affects GDP per capita,' suggesting that there is evidence to reject the null hypothesis, indicating a significant difference in means between at least two of the groups.

In summary, this code snippet is **performing an ANOVA test to assess whether the country has a significant effect on the 'GDP per capita values for the countries 'USA', 'China', and 'India'** and prints the result based on a significance level of 0.05.

Introduction to Julius

Julius (https://julius.ai/) is an AI tool dedicated to data analysis. It can help us **generate plots, graphs, charts, pivot tables, and so on**. It can also clean and prepare the data for usage. To summarize, it helps with **data cleaning, data preprocessing, data visualization, and many more without the need to write any code**. We can just upload the Excel or CSV or any data file and ask questions on the file, and voila we get the results.

Overview of Julius as an AI Tool

Julius turns hours of Excel work into minutes. The features of Julius are **data visualizations, data cleaning and preprocessing, creating animations, complex statistical modeling**, and of course asking questions like **we use prompts in ChatGPT, Bard, or Phind**.

A demo of the website is presented in *Figure 8.8*.

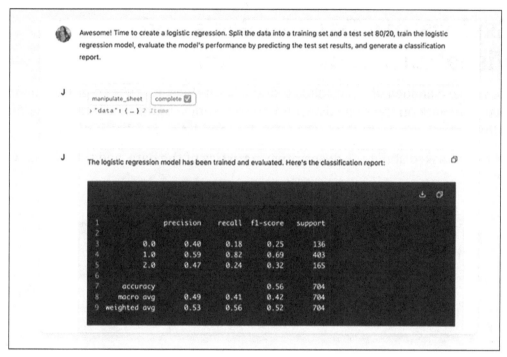

Figure 8.8: *A demo of Julius on how a user gives a prompt and gets a result*

We can see from the preceding screenshot that the user asks to **create a logistic regression model and then create a classification report**. Of course, as always, **the more detailed and specific the prompt, the better the result we get**. So, the user instructs **Julius to split the data into training and test data** and get the report. We see that the **classification report** is generated accurately as instructed. And, **we do not need to code** at all, but **we need to know how things work in the background** so that **we can give better-quality prompts for accurate results**.

There are these use cases for **Energy data analysis over time** and for **generating patient insights.** These are very good use cases if one chooses to use the tool and focus on analyzing the data for a particular domain like healthcare, energy, finance, retail, marketing, HR, and so on.

https://julius.ai/use_cases/energy

https://julius.ai/use_cases#/patients

Exploratory Data Analysis and Visualization using Julius

So, we have an idea of what Julius is and what it does. It's time to get our hands dirty and work on the same data, and spit out some results. Let's start by **asking Julius some basic facts about the GDP data and let's see what it gives us**.

Julius was asked about the **descriptive statistics of the data,** and this is what we get.

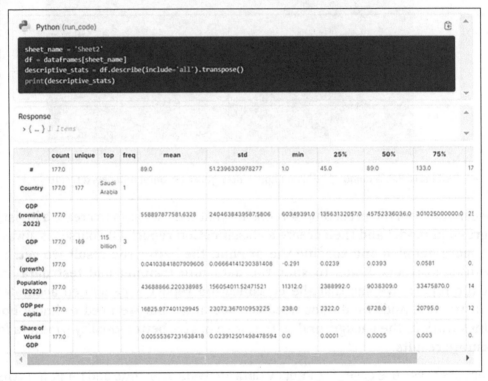

Figure 8.9: *Descriptive Statistics of the data by Julius*

The code was written by Julius ,and it is the same what we wrote earlier. It saves us a lot of man-hours. Let's see what the summarization Julius wrote for us.

The descriptive statistics for the dataset have been calculated. Here's a summary of the findings:

- The '#' column has values **ranging from 1 to 177**, with a **mean of 89**, indicating it's likely an index or ranking.

- There are **177 unique countries listed**.

- The 'GDP (nominal, 2022) column shows a wide range in GDP values, with a **mean of approximately 558.9 billion** and a **maximum of 25.46 trillion**, suggesting significant variation in country economies.

- The **'GDP (growth)' column has values between –29.1% and 57.8%,** with a **mean growth of 4.1%**.

- Population figures also vary widely, with a **mean of approximately 43.7 million and a significant standard deviation, indicating a diverse set of countries in terms of population size.**

The distributions of **GDP (nominal, 2022), Population (2022), and GDP per capita** have been visualized:

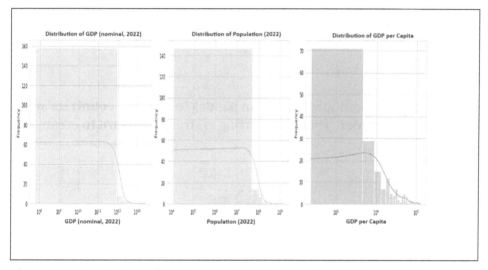

Figure 8.10: *Distributions of GDP (nominal, 2022), Population (2022), and GDP per capita*

- The **GDP (nominal, 2022) distribution shows a right-skewed pattern**, indicating that a **few countries have a very high GDP while the majority have a lower GDP.**

- The **Population (2022) distribution is also right-skewed**, suggesting that **most countries have a smaller population, with a few countries having a very large population**.

- The **GDP per capita distribution appears to be right-skewed as well**, with **most countries having a lower GDP per capita and fewer countries with a high GDP per capita.**

The results we got can't be any better. The tool has explained everything in detail, and we need not ask anything. It is indeed a gem when it comes to data analysis and visualization.

We will see the **code and pie chart created by Julius** to show the **%share of GDP by the top 10 nations with the maximum nominal GDP**.

```
# Sorting the dataframe by GDP (nominal, 2022) to get the top 10 countries
top_countries = df.sort_values(by='GDP (nominal, 2022)', ascending=False).
head(10)
# Plotting the pie chart for the % share of World GDP of the top 10
countries
plt.figure(figsize=(10, 10))
plt.pie(top_countries['Share of World GDP'], labels=top_countries
['Country'], autopct='%1.1f%%', startangle=140)
plt.title('Top 10 Countries by % Share of World GDP')
plt.axis('equal')   # Equal aspect ratio ensures that pie is drawn as a
circle.
plt.show()
```

The **.sort_values()** method is used from pandas to have the **countries' nominal GDP in descending order**. Then the plotting is straightforward to create the pie chart.

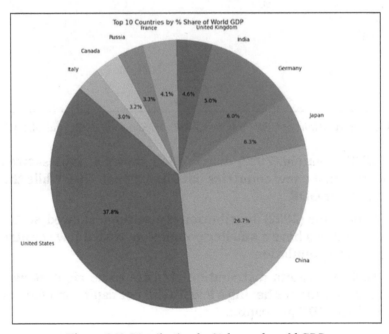

Figure 8.11: *Distribution by %share of world GDP*

Approximately **99% of the world's GDP is acquired by these 10 nations**. There is a stark imbalance in **wealth distribution and the poorer countries are still poor.**

Next, we see the GDP per capita of the top 10 countries.

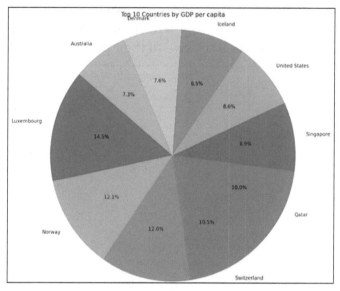

Figure 8.12: *Distribution by GDP per capita*

From the preceding pie chart, we can see that most of the **countries are European and they have a very high standard of living** which is reflected by the **amount of money each citizen possesses (GDP per capita)**. Qatar is an **oil-rich nation, and Singapore and the US are developed too**.

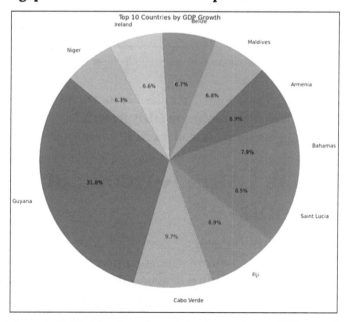

Figure 8.13: *Distribution of countries by maximum GDP growth*

From the preceding pie chart, we can see that **all the nations are smaller in size**, that is, **less population that's why we can see high GDP growth**. This visualization helps to quickly identify which **countries are experiencing the most rapid economic expansion** relative to their peers.

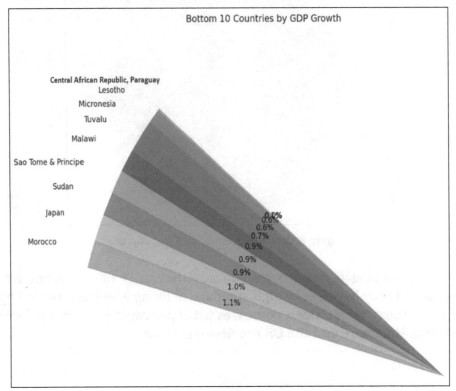

Figure 8.14: *Distribution of countries by least GDP growth*

We can see some countries from Africa like **Morocco, Sudan, and the Central African Republic** that have the **minimum GDP growth**. But it is surprising to see **Japan** on the list and its **economy is contracting every year or getting slower**.

Data Analysis Using No-code or Low-code Tools

In the realm of data analysis, the emergence of **no-code and low-code tools** has revolutionized the way businesses operate and make decisions. These tools have **democratized data analysis, making it accessible not only to data scientists and IT professionals but also to individuals across various departments.**

No-code tools are platforms that allow **users to develop applications or**

perform complex tasks without writing a single line of code. They typically use a graphical user interface, such as drag-and-drop builders, to enable non-technical users to create applications or analyze data.

Low-code tools, on the other hand, **require some coding** but **significantly less than traditional development methods**. They provide **pre-built components and a visual interface for application development, reducing the amount of hand-coding required** and accelerating the development process.

There are tools such as **Gigasheet, Mito, PivotTableJS, Drawdata, PyGWalker, Visual Python, TF Playground, and ydata-Profiling** that are no-code tools. These tools are very useful for data science-based projects and **improve efficiency and productivity.** We will look into these tools with some characteristics of each tool and some demos.

Gigasheet

Gigasheet is a browser-based no-code tool used to analyze data. It can take **up to 1 billion+ rows and uses AI to do data analysis**. It is a combination of Excel and Pandas with a lot of room for data consumption. It can also be used to do **group, plot, merge, sort, and descriptive statistics**.

It also imports data from **AWS S3, Drive, databases, Excel**, and more.

Gigasheet also provides an API that helps in **automating repetitive tasks and scheduling imports and exports**.

Mito

Mito is an open-source tool that analyzes the data within a spreadsheet interface in Jupyter Notebook without writing any code. It helps in code generation.

The installation process is as follows:

```
!python -m pip install mitosheet
```

The activation process is as follows; we write these two commands in Jupyter.

```
!python -m jupyter nbextension install --py --user mitosheet
!python -m jupyter nbextension enable --py --user mitosheet
```

The format of the data looks like this. We have to install **mitosheet and mitosheet.sheet().**

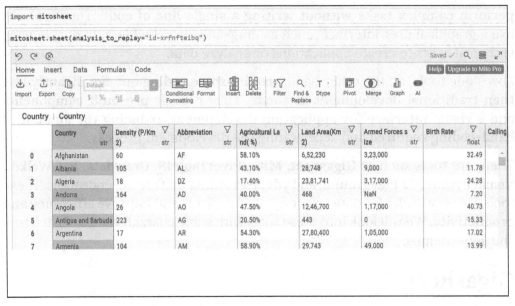

Figure 8.15: *Mitosheet data representation*

We can also give prompts by **clicking the AI option to obtain results**. The screenshot of the representation is as follows.

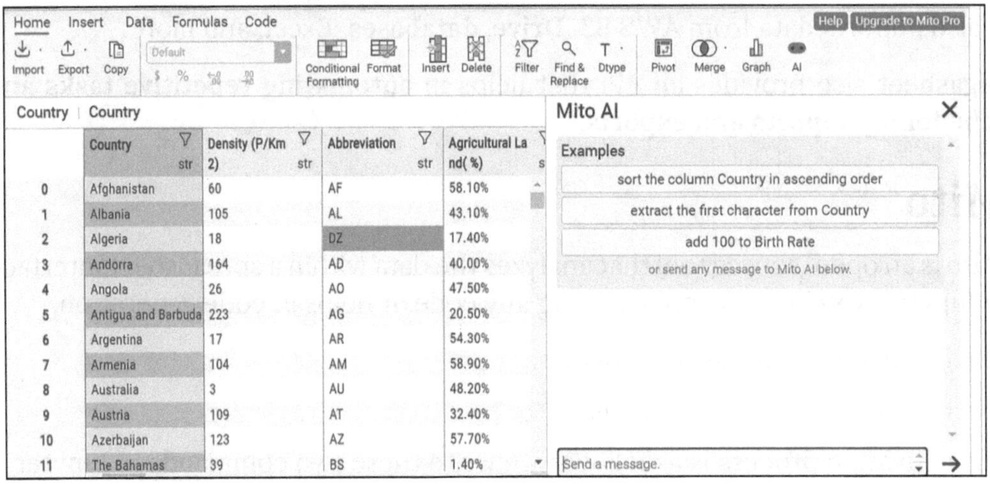

Figure 8.16: *Mitosheet data representation with AI support option*

This is the automatic code generated by Mito.

```
from mitosheet.public.v3 import *; # Analysis Name:id-xrfnfteibq;

import pandas as pd

# Imported Sheet2 from GDP data.xlsx
```

```
sheet_df_dictonary = pd.read_excel(r'GDP data.xlsx', engine='openpyxl',
sheet_name=['Sheet2'], skiprows=0)
Sheet2 = sheet_df_dictonary['Sheet2']
```

PivotTableJS

PivotTableJS creates Pivot Tables, aggregations, and charts for Jupyter Notebooks. The representation is as follows.

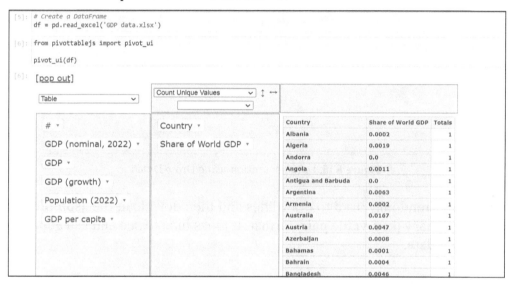

Figure 8.17: *PivotTable JS representation of the data*

In the preceding screenshot, we have created a Pivot Table using the PivotTable JS tool. It is a very handy tool when it comes to generating pivots and aggregations.

Drawdata

Drawdata is a tool that draws datasets in Jupyter. We need to install the **drawdata** package.

```
!python -m pip install drawdata
```

The code for drawing the data is as follows.

```
from drawdata import draw_scatter
draw_scatter()
```

The **draw_scatter() function** is used to create the data and then we can download it from Jupyter.

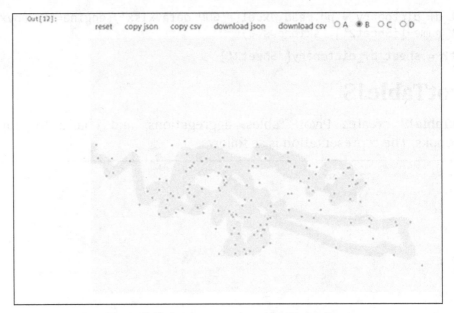

Figure 8.18: *Data generation using Draw Data*

The pen was randomly used to draw lines and then download the **.json file**. It is in the **dictionary (key, value pair)** format. It looks nice to see and is a **good tool to generate data.**

PyGWalker

PyGWalker is an open-source tool that can transform pandas data frame into a tableau-style interface for data exploration. The code we use is as follows.

```
!pip install pygwalker
import pygwalker as pyg
walker = pyg.walk(df)
```

We need to install the **pygwalker library** and then **import the pygwalker function**. The **.walk() method** is used to create the Tableau interface.

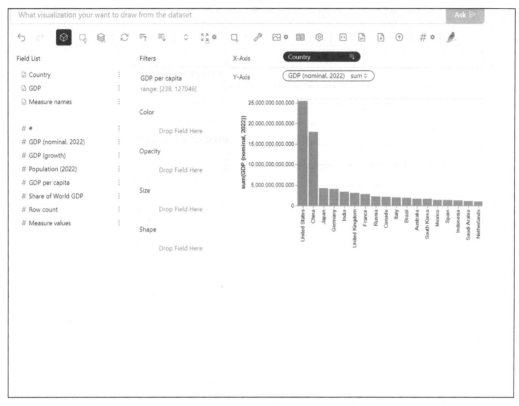

Figure 8.19: *The Tableau interface created by PyGWalker*

The preceding screenshot shows that the created interface looks exactly like Tableau. The **nominal GDP for each nation is shown in descending order**.

It is an excellent tool when we want to experiment with various kinds of visualization on Jupyter, and it just uses a few lines of code to create the interface.

Visual Python

Visual Python is a GUI-based Python code generator for data science, an extension to Jupyter Lab, Jupyter Notebook, and Google Colab.

https://visualpython.ai/visualpython-desktop

There are also a few more tools, such as **pandas-profiling, d-tale, sweetviz, and autoviz,** that were explained and demonstrated in detail, in the first few chapters. We can also try those tools.

https://opendatascience.com/top-low-code-and-no-code-platforms-for-data-science-in-2023/

https://www.linkedin.com/pulse/rise-no-codelow-code-data-analysis-tools-insights-every-shivam-bansal/

https://www.blog.dailydoseofds.com/p/8-immensely-powerful-no-code-tools

https://www.blog.dailydoseofds.com/p/gigasheet-effortlessly-analyse-upto

https://www.blog.dailydoseofds.com/p/mito-just-got-supercharged-with-ai

https://www.blog.dailydoseofds.com/p/a-no-code-tool-to-create-charts-and

https://www.blog.dailydoseofds.com/p/drawdata-the-coolest-tool-to-create

https://www.blog.dailydoseofds.com/p/the-pandas-dataframe-extension-every

https://www.blog.dailydoseofds.com/p/this-gui-tool-can-possibly-save-you

Conclusion

Utilizing Python to **analyze real-world data sets allows us to gain valuable insights and make data-driven decisions**. Python, being a versatile and widely-used language, offers various **libraries and tools that can streamline and simplify the process of data analysis**.

Throughout the chapter, we learned how to use libraries like **pandas for data manipulation and seaborn for data visualization**. We saw how these tools can be **used in conjunction with Python to load, clean, preprocess, and visualize data, making it easier to understand and interpret.**

We have worked on a **real-world dataset on the GDP of nations and came up with a lot of data-driven insights**. We also performed **statistical data analysis along with Exploratory Data analysis**.

Moreover, we also tried our hands on AI, no-code, and low-code tools, such as **Julius, PyGWalker, Visual Python, PivotTable JS, Draw Data, Mito,** and so on. These are **very efficient** and **productive to work with and save a lot of human hours per week**. In the next and final chapter, we will look into the appendix which will contain various **Python functions and packages that are essential for Python programming and data science.**

A Python Cheat Sheet

Introduction

This is the last chapter of this book, and here, we will see the functions that are used in Python, be it from a data analytics perspective or a simple programming perspective. It will be a comprehensive cheat sheet that will have a condensed overview of Python's syntax, keywords, data types, built-in functions, and other relevant things.

Python is a very flexible programming language, has a large community of contributors, its simplicity and readability, and its applications from web development to artificial intelligence. The cheat sheet in this chapter will be very handy for your Python usage, whether you are a fresher or a professional in the industry who needs a brush up on the concepts.

The cheat sheet will have the functions on Python programming basics, the various data types, the control structures, functions, classes, and more concepts. There are also techniques like Python file handling and exceptions, and deep dive into the libraries and tools needed to build Data Science products and Artificial Intelligence applications.

Remember, while this cheat sheet provides a solid foundation, the best way to learn Python is by building projects, practicing interview questions, and open-source contributions. Use this guide as a starting point; don't be afraid to experiment, make mistakes, and learn from them. Happy coding!

Structure

In this chapter, we will discuss the following topics:

- Python Basics
  - Python syntax and keywords
  - Python data types
  - Creating, naming, and using variables
  - Arithmetic, comparison, logical, and assignment operators
  - Creating single and multi-line comments
- Control Structures
  - Conditional statements
  - Loops and control statements like break, continue, and pass
- Data Structures
  - Lists
  - Tuples
  - Dictionaries
  - Sets
- Functions
  - Defining functions
  - The anonymous lambda function
  - Built-in functions
- Object Oriented Programming System (OOPS)
  - Defining classes, creating objects, instance variables, and methods
- Exceptions
  - Defining exceptions, handling exceptions using try, except, finally

Python Basics

Python basics include the basic Python syntax and keywords, the datatypes present like Boolean, numeric, and string, creating naming, and using the variables, the operators of arithmetic, logical, comparison, and assignment, and creating single and multi-line comments. These concepts are used daily by any Python programmer. These form the foundations of Python programming.

The Python built-in keywords are as follows:

```
False, Class, finally, is, return, None, continue, for, lambda, try,
True, def, from, nonlocal, while, and, del, global, not, with, as, elif,
if, or, yield, assert, else, import, pass, break, except, in, raise
```

For the various Python data types, there are **numeric, complex, boolean, and object (string)**.

```
x = 10  # int

y = 20.5  # float

z = 1j  # complex

s = "hello"  # str

b = True  # bool
```

Python variables are created when a value is assigned to them. It is straightforward, but some rules need to be followed while creating a variable. **Variable names in Python can be any length and can consist of uppercase and lowercase letters (A-Z, a-z), digits (0-9), and the underscore character (_)**. However, they cannot start with a digit.

```
x = 5

y = "John"

print(x)

print(y)
```

For **Arithmetic Operators**, there are +,-,*,/,%,**, and //.

For **Logical Operators**, there are **and, or, and not keywords**.

For **Comparison Operators**, there are **==, !=, >, <, >=, and <= symbols**.

For **Assignment Operators**, there are =,+=, -=, *=,/=,%=,//=, **=,&=,|=, ^=, >>=, and <<=

```
x = 5 (Assignment Operator)

x+=5 (Addition Assignment) #Equivalent to x =x+5

x-=5 (Subtraction Assignment) #Equivalent to x =x-5

x*=5 (Multiplication Assignment) #Equivalent to x =x*5

x/=5 (Division Assignment) #Equivalent to x =x/5

x//=5 (Floor Division assignment) # Equivalent to x =x //5

x%=5 (Modulus Assignment) #Equivalent to x =x%5 (Gives the remainder of
the division)
```

```
x**=5 (Exponentiation Assignment) #Equivalent to x = x**5
#(Raises the variable to the power of the value on the right)
```

We can use the # symbol for single-line comments, and " or "" for multi-line comments.

```
# This is a single-line comment


'''
This is a
multi-line comment
'''




"""""
This is also a
multi-line comment
"""""
```

Control Structures

Python control structures have conditional statements like **if, elif, and else statements** to satisfy certain conditions. The Flow structure is as follows:

```
x = 10
if x > 5:
    print("x is greater than 5")
```

If we check the **elif** statement, then:

```
x = 10
if x > 10:
    print("x is greater than 10")
elif x == 10:
    print("x is equal to 10")
'''
```

Either the **1st condition is fulfilled** using the **if statement** or the **next condition** is fulfilled using the **elif statement.** If none of the conditions are met, nothing will be printed. If we want to print in case none of the conditions are met then we can also add an **else statement** as follows:

```
x = 10
if x > 10:
    print("x is greater than 10")
elif x == 10:
    print("x is equal to 10")
else:
    print("X is less than 10")
```

There are only the **if condition** and **the else condition**, either one will be fulfilled and there is no need for the **elif** statement in this case.

Two loops are used in Python: **while** and **for** loops.

While loop

```
i = 1
while i <= 10:
        print(i)
        i += 1
```

The while loop **iterates over a block and adds till the number reaches 10**. If **i+=1** is not used, then the loop goes into an infinite loop and the loop will keep going.

For loop

```
for i in range(1, 11):
        print(i)
```

The **for loop** in Python iterates over a sequence (be it a list, tuple, or string). The range function in this case gives **1 to 10** as the output, excluding 11.

Control Statements

There are statements like **break, continue, and pass statements** that are used to leave the loop or continue with the next iteration.

```
# Using break in a while loop

counter = 0

while True:
    print(f"Current counter value: {counter}")

    # Break the loop when counter reaches 3
    if counter == 3:
        print("Breaking out of the loop.")
        break

    # Increment the counter
    counter += 1

# Output:
# Current counter value: 0
# Current counter value: 1
# Current counter value: 2
# Current counter value: 3
# Breaking out of the loop.
```

In the code, the **while True** creates an infinite loop. The **break statement** exits the loop when the **counter variable** reaches 3.

The **continue keyword** in Python is used in for and while loops to **skip the rest of the code inside the loop for the current iteration and move to the next iteration.**

```
# Example: Skip odd numbers in a loop

for i in range(1, 11):
    # Skip even numbers
    if i % 2 != 0:
        continue
```

```
    # This part of the code will be skipped for odd numbers
    print(f"Even number: {i}")
```

```
print("Loop finished")
```

The for loop iterates from 1 to 10. Then an if statement is used to check for odd numbers, and the **continue keyword** is found. The code inside the loop for the current iteration is skipped and moved to the next iteration.

Then only even numbers are printed, and the **Loop finished statement is printed**. The **continue statement helps control the flow of the loop by skipping specific iterations** based on a condition.

The **pass keyword** is placed as a block of code when we are not executing any operation.

```
def process_data(data):
    # Check if the data is valid
    if data is None:
        # If data is None, do nothing for now
        pass
    else:
        # Process the data
        print(f"Processing data: {data}")
```

```
# Example usage
process_data(None)
process_data("Hello, World!")
```

In the example, the **process_data()** function checks if the provided **data is None**. The **pass statement** is used to show that no action needs to be taken.

Data Structures

Data Structures in Python are primarily **lists, dictionaries, sets, tuples, and strings**. There are methods for each data structure which we will list down. They are all built-in and offer various functionalities while applying.

List

Lists are a collection of **heterogeneous elements (like integer, float, boolean, string data type)** inside square brackets separated by commas.

```
numbers = [1, 2, 3, 4, 10]
names = ['Jenny', 'Sam', 'Alexis']
mixed = ['Jenny', 1, 2]
list_of_lists = [['a', 1], ['b', 2]]
```

The `list_of_lists` variable is also called a **nested list (a list within a list)**.

There are several methods for lists mentioned as follows with examples and explanations.

- **append(x):** Adds an element x to the end of the list `my_list`.

```
my_list = [1, 2, 3]
my_list.append(4)
print(my_list)
# Output: [1, 2, 3, 4]
```

- **extend(x):** Extends the list by appending elements from the iterable.

```
my_list = [1, 2, 3]
my_list.extend([4, 5, 6])
print(my_list)
# Output: [1, 2, 3, 4, 5, 6]
```

- **insert(i, x): Inserts element x** at the **specified index i** in the list `my_list`.

```
my_list = [1, 2, 3]
my_list.insert(1, 4)
print(my_list)
# Output: [1, 4, 2, 3]
```

- **remove(x):** Removes the **first occurrence of element x** from the list `my_list`.

```
my_list = [1, 2, 3, 2]
my_list.remove(2)
print(my_list)
# Output: [1, 3, 2]
```

- **pop([i])**: Removes and returns the element at index **i**. If **i** is not provided, it removes the last element and returns.

```python
my_list = [1, 2, 3]
popped_element = my_list.pop(1)
print(popped_element)


# Output: 2
```

- **index(x)**: Returns the index of the **first occurrence of element x**.

```python
my_list = [1, 2, 3, 2]
index_of_2 = my_list.index(2)
print(index_of_2)


# Output: 1
```

- **count(x)**: Returns the **number of occurrences of element x** in the list.

```python
my_list = [1, 2, 3, 2]
count_of_2 = my_list.count(2)
print(count_of_2)


# Output: 2
```

- **sort()**: Sorts the list elements in the ascending order.

```python
my_list = [3, 1, 4, 1, 5, 9, 2]
my_list.sort()
print(my_list)


# Output: [1, 1, 2, 3, 4, 5, 9]
```

- **reverse()**: Reverses the elements of the list.

```python
my_list = [1, 2, 3]
my_list.reverse()
print(my_list)


# Output: [3, 2, 1]
```

Tuple

Tuples are **immutable data types**, meaning we can't modify a tuple's elements after it is created.

- **count(x)**: Returns the **number of occurrences of an element x** present in the tuple.

```
my_tuple = (1, 2, 3, 2, 4, 2, 5)
count_of_2 = my_tuple.count(2)
print(count_of_2)


# Output: 3
```

- **index(x[,start[,end]])**: Returns the index of the first occurrence of the specified valued x in the tuple. One can also provide the start and end parameters to specify the search range.

```
my_tuple = (10, 20, 30, 20, 40, 20, 50)
index_of_20 = my_tuple.index(20)
print(index_of_20)


# Output: 1


# Specifying start and end parameters
my_tuple = (10, 20, 30, 20, 40, 20, 50)
index_of_20_after_index_2 = my_tuple.index(20, 2)
print(index_of_20_after_index_2)


# Output: 3
```

Dictionaries

Dictionaries are data structures that are in the form of key-value pairs. The keys are indexed normally and are unique. Dictionaries are represented by "{}" and consist of key-value pairs separated by colons.

Here are some of the methods that dictionaries can use.

- **clear()**: It removes all items from a dictionary.

```python
my_dict = {'a': 1, 'b': 2, 'c': 3}
my_dict.clear()
print(my_dict)


# Output: {}
```

- **copy()**: Returns a shallow copy of the dictionary.

```python
original_dict = {'a': 1, 'b': 2, 'c': 3}
copied_dict = original_dict.copy()
print(copied_dict)


# Output: {'a': 1, 'b': 2, 'c': 3}
```

- **get(key[,default])**: Returns the value for the specified key. If the key is not found, it returns the **default value or None** if not provided.

```python
my_dict = {'a': 1, 'b': 2, 'c': 3}
value_of_b = my_dict.get('b')
print(value_of_b)


# Output: 2


value_of_d = my_dict.get('d', 'Key not found')
print(value_of_d)


# Output: 'Key not found'
```

- **items()**: Returns the contents of the dictionary in the form of tuples.

```python
my_dict = {'a': 1, 'b': 2, 'c': 3}
dict_items = my_dict.items()
print(dict_items)


# Output: dict_items([('a', 1), ('b', 2), ('c', 3)])
```

- **keys()**: Gives the dictionary's keys.

```
my_dict = {'a': 1, 'b': 2, 'c': 3}
dict_keys = my_dict.keys()
print(dict_keys)


# Output: dict_keys(['a', 'b', 'c'])
```

- **values()**: Gives the dictionary's values

```
my_dict = {'a': 1, 'b': 2, 'c': 3}
dict_values = my_dict.values()
print(dict_values)


# Output: dict_values([1, 2, 3])
```

- **pop(key[,default])**: Removes the elements with the specific key and returns the value of it. If the key is not found, it raises a **KeyError** or returns the default value if provided.

```
my_dict = {'a': 1, 'b': 2, 'c': 3}
popped_value = my_dict.pop('b')
print(popped_value)


# Output: 2


# Using default value
my_dict = {'a': 1, 'b': 2, 'c': 3}
popped_value = my_dict.pop('d', 'Key not found')
print(popped_value)


# Output: 'Key not found'
```

- **popitem()**: Removes and returns the last inserted key-value pair as a tuple.

```
my_dict = {'a': 1, 'b': 2, 'c': 3}
popped_item = my_dict.popitem()
print(popped_item)


# Output: ('c', 3)
```

- **update([other])**: Updates the dictionary with key-value pairs from another dictionary or an iterable of key-value pairs.

```
my_dict = {'a': 1, 'b': 2, 'c': 3}
new_dict = {'b': 4, 'd': 5}
my_dict.update(new_dict)
print(my_dict)


# Output: {'a': 1, 'b': 4, 'c': 3, 'd': 5}
```

- **setdefault(key[,default])**: Returns the value for the specific key. If the key is not found, it **inserts the key with the default value or None** if not provided.

```
my_dict = {'a': 1, 'b': 2, 'c': 3}
value_of_d = my_dict.setdefault('d', 0)
print(value_of_d)


# Output: 0
```

Sets

Sets are an unordered collection of data types that can be **iterated and mutated** and contain no duplicate elements.

```
S = {1,2,3} #this is a set
```

Some methods used in sets are as follows.

- **add(element)**: Adds the specified element to the set.

```
my_set = {1, 2, 3}
my_set.add(4)
print(my_set)


# Output: {1, 2, 3, 4}
```

- **update(iterable)**: Adds elements from an iterable (for example, list, set) to the set.

```
my_set = {1, 2, 3}
my_set.update([3, 4, 5])
print(my_set)


# Output: {1, 2, 3, 4, 5}
```

- **remove(element):** Removes the specified element from the set. Raises a **KeyError** if the element is not present.

```
my_set = {1, 2, 3, 4, 5}
my_set.remove(3)
print(my_set)


# Output: {1, 2, 4, 5}
```

- **discard(element):** Removes the specified element from the set if it is present. Does not raise an error if the element is not found.

```
my_set = {1, 2, 3, 4, 5}
my_set.discard(3)
print(my_set)


# Output: {1, 2, 4, 5}
```

- **pop():** Removes and returns an arbitrary element from the set. Raises a **KeyError** if the set is empty.

```
my_set = {1, 2, 3, 4, 5}
popped_element = my_set.pop()
print(popped_element)


print(my_set)
# Output: (an arbitrary element)
# Output: the set without the popped element
```

- **clear():** Removes all the elements from the set.

```
my_set = {1, 2, 3, 4, 5}
my_set.clear()
print(my_set)


# Output: set()
```

- **union (other set) or | operator:** Returns a new set containing all the (unique) elements from both sets.

```
set1 = {1, 2, 3}
set2 = {3, 4, 5}
union_set = set1.union(set2)
```

```
    # Alternatively: union_set = set1 | set2
    print(union_set)


    # Output: {1, 2, 3, 4, 5}
```

- **Intersection (other set) or & operator:** Returns a new set containing common elements of both sets.

```
    set1 = {1, 2, 3, 4}
    set2 = {3, 4, 5, 6}
    intersection_set = set1.intersection(set2)


    # Alternatively: intersection_set = set1 & set2


    print(intersection_set)
    # Output: {3, 4}
```

Functions

A function in Python is created using the **def** keyword, followed by the **function name**, and then having a **set of parentheses containing the parameters**. Its main purpose is to break a problem into smaller pieces and reuse the code later.

Defining functions

Here is a basic example to understand how functions in Python work.

```
def add_numbers(num1, num2):
    sum = num1 + num2
    return sum
```

The function name is **add_numbers** and has the **parameters num1 and num2** to add them. The purpose is to add both numbers. The **sum variable** is returned at the end.

We can call the function by:

```
print(add_numbers(3, 5))


# Output: 8
```

We need to use the function **add_numbers** and pass to numbers like 3 and 5 in this case. The result is the addition of both numbers.

Lambda Anonymous Function

The lambda function is used to create an anonymous short-lived function. It is created using the `lambda` keyword, **followed by parameters and expression**. It is used in situations when creating a function using the `def` keyword will be redundant.

```python
# Regular function definition
def add(x, y):
    return x + y


# Equivalent lambda function
lambda_add = lambda x, y: x + y


# Using both functions
result1 = add(3, 5)
result2 = lambda_add(3, 5)

print("Result from regular function:", result1)
print("Result from lambda function:", result2)
```

In the preceding code snippet, **add** is a normal function and **lambda_add** is the equivalent lambda function.

Lambda functions are also used with functions like **map()**, **filter()**, or **sorted()**.

```python
# List of tuples representing names and ages
people = [("Akshay", 25), ("Ravi", 15), ("Rahul", 35)]


# Sort the list of tuples based on the second element (age)
sorted_people = sorted(people, key=lambda person: person[1])


print("Sorted People:", sorted_people)
```

In the preceding code, the lambda function is used as a **key** argument for the **sorted()** function.

The lambda function extracts the second element (index 1) of each tuple, that is, the age.

The result of the code is as follows.

```
Sorted People: [('Ravi', 15), ('Akshay', 25), ('Rahul', 35)]
```

The sorted list of tuples has the elements in the ascending order of their ages.

Built-in functions

Built-in functions are the ones that are already provided in the Python compiler when we install it. Python has a lot of built-in functions as follows:

- **print()**: Prints the specified message to the screen.
- **len()**: Returns the length of an object.
- **type()**: Returns the type of an object.
- **str()**, **int()**, **float()**: Convert object types.
- **range()**: Generates a sequence of numbers.
- **list()**, **tuple()**, **dict()**, **set()**: Convert to list, tuple, dictionary, set.
- **input()**: Allows user input.

There are also a lot of other built-in functions that help perform operations to solve problems.

Object Oriented Programming System

Object Oriented Programming System (OOPS) is a programming system that uses **objects, classes, and methods** to **create and organize code**. In Python, everything is an object.

Defining classes, creating objects, instance variables, and methods

Classes in Python are the main tree for creating objects. An object is an instance of a class. A class defines attributes and behaviors common to all objects of that type.

We will see a reference code to understand the concepts one by one.

```python
# Defining a class in Python
class Vehicle:
    # This is the constructor
    def __init__(self, name, color):
        self.name = name  # Instance variable
        self.color = color  # Instance variable


    # This is an instance method
    def get_info(self):
        return f"Vehicle [Name: {self.name}, Color: {self.color}]"


# Inheritance in Python
class Car(Vehicle):
    def __init__(self, name, color, company):
        # Calling the constructor of the parent class
        super().__init__(name, color)
        self.company = company  # Additional instance variable


    # Overriding the get_info method
    def get_info(self):
        return f"Car [Name: {self.name}, Color: {self.color}, Company:
{self.company}]"


# Creating an object (instance of a class)
vehicle = Vehicle("Vehicle1", "Red")
print(vehicle.get_info())  # Output: Vehicle [Name: Vehicle1, Color:
Red]


# Creating an object of the derived class
car = Car("Car1", "Blue", "Company1")
print(car.get_info())  # Output: Car [Name: Car1, Color: Blue, Company:
Company1]
```

In the preceding Python program:

- **Vehicle** is a class that has two instance variables: **name and color** and one instance method: `get_info`.

- **Car** is a class that inherits from the **Vehicle** class. It adds an instance variable: **company** and overrides the `get_info` method.

- An **instance (or object)** of a class is created by calling the class (like a function call) and passing any required arguments to the `__init__` method.

- Instance methods are **functions that are part of the class**, and they **can access the instance variables of the class**.

- **Inheritance** is a mechanism where a **new class is derived from an existing class**. The **derived class (child class)** inherits the **properties and methods of the base class** (parent class).

- Polymorphism in Python is demonstrated by **overriding methods in the derived class**. The **derived class** can provide its **implementation of methods that are already provided by the base class**.

Exceptions

Exceptions in Python are the situations that can modify the control flow through the program. They get initiated on errors and they show up in the code. They are handled by the four keywords (**try**, **except**, **finally**, and **raise**), the assert statement, and the Python interpreter.

Defining exceptions, handling exceptions using try, except, and finally

The **try** block lets test the block of code for errors, the **except** block handles the error, and the **finally** block executes the code, regardless of the result of the try and except blocks.

Here is an example code.

```
try:
    print(1 / 0)
except ZeroDivisionError:
    print('You cannot divide by zero!')
 finally:
    print('This line of code will always be executed.')
```

We are **operating division by 0**, and we give the `ZeroDivisionError` under the **except block.**

We can raise exceptions using the raise keyword. It's often used with an exception type or exception instance as an argument.

```
raise ValueError('A value error happened.')
```

We can catch **multiple exceptions** by providing a tuple of exception types in the **except** clause.

```
try:
    # code that may raise an exception
except (TypeError, ValueError) as e:
    print(f'Caught an exception: {e}')
```

Python has several built-in exceptions, such as `IndexError, TypeError, ValueError, ZeroDivisionError, FileNotFoundError,` and so on. Every error has its scenario of occurrence.

Conclusion

This marks the end of the cheat sheet on Python, where we have covered the Python basics to various operators to control structures to loops to data types to data structures and their functions to how to define functions, the lambda function, the OOPS (Object Oriented Programming Systems) and Exceptions. We had already covered a lot of functions on **pandas, numpy, matplotlib, seaborn, statsmodels**, and so on, to show data analysis, data cleaning, data visualization, and statistical analysis in the previous chapters.

In the previous chapters, we also covered Web scraping using `BeautifulSoup,` `Selenium,` and `Pandas` to scrap data from various websites. We also included Time Series Analysis and the relevant packages involved, along with some automated tools. We also covered some **no-code and low-code tools like Julius, d-tale, pandas-profiling, sweetviz, PyGWalker**, and so on.

I hope I have done a fine job in writing the book, and even more, I hope my readers will be very satisfied and grow in their careers after reading this book. I am always open to suggestions and positive criticism so that I can learn and contribute more.

References

- https://static.realpython.com/python-cheat-sheet.pdf
- https://ehmatthes.github.io/pcc_3e/cheat_sheets/
- https://www.codewithharry.com/notes/
- https://www.datacamp.com/cheat-sheet/getting-started-with-python-cheat-sheet
- https://ehmatthes.github.io/pcc_3e/
- https://hackr.io/blog/python-cheat-sheet
- https://www.pythoncheatsheet.org/cheatsheet/exception-handling
- https://www.geeksforgeeks.org/python-exception-handling/
- https://realpython.com/python-exceptions/
- https://www.coursera.org/tutorials/python-exception-cheat-sheet
- https://realpython.com/python3-object-oriented-programming/
- https://www.learnbyexample.org/python-classes-and-objects/

Index

Symbols

.groupby() method 18
.isnull() 197
.isnull() function 48
.pie() method 19
.sort_values() method 18

A

Anaconda
  about 8
  environment, using 8
  installing steps 8
ARIMA (Autoregressive Integrated
    Moving Average) 156-163
ASR (Automatic Speech
    Recognition)
  about 188
  Python code,
    implementing 189-192
ASR, techniques
  Acoustic, modeling 188
  deep, learning 189
  End-to-End models 189
  feature, extraction 188
  language, modeling 188
audio data
  about 175, 176
  Python Libraries,
    manipulating 177-183

audio data, concepts
  Amplitude, Bit depth 176
  rate, sampling 176
  spectrogram 177
  Waveform 177
audio signal
  about 183
  processing techniques 183, 184
  Python, implementing 185-187
audio signal, areas
  audio effects 184
  audio synthesis 184
  data storage,
    compressing 184
  music information
    retrieval 184
  noise cancellation 184
  speech, processing 184
audio signal, MFCCs method
  Discrete Cosine Transfrom,
    applying 185
  Fourier Transform,
    applying 185
  logarithm, taking 185
  Mel filterbank, applying 185
  signal, framing 185
Augmented Dickey-Fuller
    (ADF) 129
auto time series libraries 167-169

B

band-pass filter 185
beautiful soup 21
Beautiful Soup 23, 29
BeautifulSoup 25-34

C

Convolutional Neural Networks
        (CNNs) 164
correlation matrix 83

D

data acquire, ways
  APIs, using 23
  data surveys, collecting 22
  websites, scraping 23
Data Analysis
  about 2
  decision-making
        applications 4
  decision-making, role 3
  functions, libraries
        exploring 9
  importance 2, 3
  strategies, challenges 3
  tools, techniques 5
Data Analysis, exploration
        methods
  Correlation analysis 79-82
  Data Distribution
        Analysis 76, 77
  Descriptive Statistic 74-76
  Dimensionality
        reduction 83-85
  Spearman Correlation 82, 83
Data Analysis, key steps
  data collection 4
  data, exploring 4
  data, modeling 4
  data preparation, cleaning 4
  data, visualizing 5

Data Distribution Analysis
  about 76, 77
  ECDF (Empirical Cumulative
        Distribution Function) 78
  Histogram 77
  KDE (Kernel Density Estimate) 77
  quantile quatile plot 79
data errors, fixing 46, 47
data errors, techniques
  Data Validation 47
  inconsistencies, outliers
        handling 51, 52
  missing values, handling 47-51
Data Integration
  about 64
  concat function, using 64-66
  join() function, using 68
  merge operation,
        using 66, 67
Data preparation
  about 46
  data, ensuring 69
  importance 46
Data preparation, libraries
  ftfy 69
  Polars 69
  Pyjanitor 68
Data preparation, techniques
  data comparability 70
  data consistency 70
data quality
  about 22
  dedicate libraries,
        accessing 39-42
Data Transformation
  about 56
  Normalization 59, 60
  Standardization 59
  variables, creating 56-59
Data Transformation, features
  Log transform 60-62
  square root transform 62, 63

Data Visualization 5
Data Visualization, principles
  accuracy 6
  clarity 6
  consistency 6
  contextualization 7
  interactivity 6
  relevance 6
  simplicity 6
Data Visualization, reasons
  complexity simplifies 6
  data communication,
        improving 6
  decision-making,
        enhancing 6
  facilitates data, exploring 6
  insights, patterns
        revealing 6
  supports, storytelling 6
Data Visualization, types
  Bar charts 7
  Heatmaps 7
  Histograms 7
  Line charts 7
  Pie charts 7
  Scatter plots 7
df.columns 13
df.describe() 15
df.head() 12

E

EDA, case studies
  dataset, manufacturing 100
  finance dataset 99
  healthcare dataset 99
  Retail Sales 99
EDA data exploring, types
  Bivariate analysis 87
  Cluster Analysis 89, 90
  multivariate analysis 88
  trends, patterns
        identifying 89
  Univariate analysis 86

EDA (Exploratory Data Analysis)
  about 73
  data, exploring 85
  importance 73
EDA, process steps
  data, cleaning 73
  data, collecting 73
  data, exploring 73
  hypothesis generation 74
  insight, summary 74
EDA, tools
  D-tale 91-96
  Pandas, profiling 96-98
EDA with Python,
        visualizing 198-208
Ensuring data quality 43
Ensuring data quality, steps
  Data Integration 44
  Data Validation 43
Exponential
        Smoothing 152, 154
extract_table_data() 26
extra_type object 14

F

Ftfy 45

H

Huggingface 189
HuggingFace 171
Hypothesis Testing
  about 124, 125
  Analysis of Variance
        (ANOVA) 127
  Chi-Square test 126
  independent t-test 125, 126
  Regression Analysis 128
Hypothesis Testing, statistics
  coefficients 128
  F-statistic 129
  p-value 129
  R-squared statistic 129
  t-statistic 129

I

Inter-Quartile Range (IQR)
     Technique 52, 53

J

Julius
  about 208
  AI tool, using 208, 209
  data analysis,
      visualizing 210-214
  no-code, low-code
      tools 214, 215
  statistics 210, 211
Julius, characteristics
  Drawdata 217, 218
  Gigasheet 215
  Mito 215, 216
  PivotTableJS 217
  PyGWalker 218, 219
  Visual Python 219
Jupyter Notebook, functionalities
  Edit option 11
  File option 10
  Insert option 11
  View option 11

K

Kurtosis 115

L

librosa 178
Librosa 177, 186
librosa.fft_frequencies() 180
LinearRegression 205

M

Margin 49-52
minds variable 191

N

np.log() function 61
Numpy 45

P

pairplot() function 88
Pandas 45
pandas.read_html() 21, 23, 36, 38
pd.read_csv() function 12
pipeline() function 192
Polars 45
Principal Component Analysis
     (PCA) 83
Probability distributions 116
Probability distributions, types
  binomial distribution 121, 122
  Lambda distribution 121
  Normal Distribution 116-118
  Poisson distribution 120
  uniform distribution 119, 120
Pyjanitor 45
PyMC3 102
pynytimes library 40
Python
  about 7
  Anaconda 8
  Matplotlib library 17

R

Real-World Datasets
  about 195, 196
  complexities,
     handling 197, 198
  Python, analyzing 194, 195
Real-World Datasets,
     characteristics
  bias subject, including 197
  Haterogeneous 196
  Large-scale 196
  messy, unstructured 196
  temporal, spatial aspects 196
Recurrent neural network
     (RNN) 164
requests 21, 23, 25, 30, 37, 38
Requests 24
requests.get() 30

S

scipy 102, 119, 120, 121
Scipy 45
Scrapy 21, 23
seasonal_decompose() function 142
selenium 21, 33
Selenium 23
Signal Processing
  about 172
  Audio signal, processing 174, 175
  Automatic Speech Recognition
      (ASR) 174
  Data Analysis,
      importance 172, 173
Simple Moving Average
    (SMA) 151, 152
skewness 50
specshow() 181
Statistical analysis
  about 103
  events predictions,
      making 132, 133
  importance 103
  techniques 105-108
  variables, determining 132
  workflow 103
Statistical analysis, libraries
  Pingouin 131
  PyMC3 131
  PyStan 131
  Scikit-learn 130
  Scipy 130
  Statsmodels 130
Statistical analysis, methods
  Descriptive statistics 108-116
  Hypothesis Testing 124, 125
  Probability distributions 116
  Statistical tests 122-124
Statistical analysis workflow, steps
  data, exploring 104
  Statistical tests 104
  variable, selecting 104

Statistical tests
  about 104
  results, interpretating 104
  visualization, reporting 104
statsmodels 102

T

Time series analysis
  about 136, 137
  Autocorrelation 146, 147
  data, visualizing 149-151
  features 137
  importance 137
  Partial Autocorrelation 147, 148
  Seasonality 141
  stationarity,
      non-stationarity 139-141
  trend, using 143-146
  White noise 148, 149
Time series analysis, types
  continuous Time series 138
  Discrete Time series 138
  Event Time series 138
  Irregular, Regular
      Time series 138
  Long format 138
  Metric Time series 138
  Multivariate Time series 138
  Panel data 138
  Univariate Time series 138
  Wide format 138
Time Series Forecasting
  about 151
  ARIMA (Autoregressive Integrated
      Moving Average) 156-163
  Autoregressive (AR) 154-156
  CNN and LSTM, learning 164
  Exponential Smoothing 152-154
  FbProphet 164
  models, evaluating 165
  parameters, exploring 165, 166
  Simple Moving Average
      (SMA) 151, 152

Time Series Forecasting,
  models
  ACF1 167
  MAPE (Mean Absolute
    Percentage Error) 166
  Mean Absolute Error
    (MAE) 166
  Mean Error (ME) 166
  Mean Squared Error
    (MSE) 166
  RMSE (Root Mean Squared
    Error) 166
Time Series Forecasting,
  parameters
  attributes, correlation 165
  seasonality 165
  Trend 165

Time series non-stationary, properties
  Augmented Dickey-Fuller
    (ADF) 139
  visual inspection 139
Time series stationary, properties
  strong stationarity 139
  weak stationarity 139
transcription 188

W

wait variable 34
web scraping
  libraries, using 23, 24
  tools, using 24-33

Z

Z-Score Technique 54-56

Made in United States
Troutdale, OR
12/30/2024

27434899R00151